CROSSWORD
a Day!

ACROSS
1 Words and music (4)
5 Erect (5)
7 Archangel (7)
8 Frisky (7)
11 Film, *Look Who's* --- (7)
13 Bonnie and ---, criminal duo (5)
14 Leg joint (4)

DOWN
1 Herb (4)
2 Aristocracy (8)
3 Tint (3)
4 Eric ---, Monty Python actor (4)
5 Two-wheeled transport (7)
6 Misapprehension (8)
9 Rear (4)
10 Leer (4)
12 Attach (3)

SOLUTION FOR DAY 15
Across 1. Hello 6. Nurse 7. Jewel 9. Mill 10. Lake 14. Route 15. Larva 16. Bushy
Down 1. Hilly 4. Orc 5. Get 8. Sketch 11. Drab 12. Elli 13. Era

CROSSWORD a Day!

ACROSS
1 Trailer (7)
6 Laid by birds (3)
7 Woman's outfit (7)
8 Castle tower (4)
9 Section (4)
12 Ethnic dialect (7)
14 Weep (3)
15 Part of the day (7)

DOWN
1 Chop (3)
2 European river (5)
3 Flower container (4)
4 Mesh (3)
5 Representative (5)
8 Rap (5)
10 Excuse (5)
11 Tibia, eg (4)
12 Look at (3)
13 Droop (3)

CROSSWORD a Day!

ACROSS
1 Greek letter (2)
2 Snake (5)
7 Unpolished (5)
8 Enjoyment (3)
9 Leave out (4)
10 Adhesive (4)
12 Heir (3)
13 Doctrinal principle (5)
14 Musical speed (5)
15 *Stand --- Me*, film (2)

DOWN
1 Sea mammal (8)
3 Arthur ---, 1970s tennis player (4)
4 Inexplicable (8)
5 People watching (8)
6 Collection of forefathers (8)
11 Cease (4)

DAY 19

CROSSWORD
a Day!

Across
2 Particular (7)
5 Magnificence (9)
7 Publish (5)
12 Forerunner (9)
14 Shoemaker (7)

Down
1 Stingy (5)
2 Daily period of unconsciousness (5)
3 Consume (3)
4 As well (4)
6 Holy sister (3)
8 Actor, --- Lowe (3)
9 Film, *Crouching ---, Hidden Dragon* (5)
10 Greek Island (5)
11 Ring of light (4)
13 Unwell (3)

CROSSWORD a Day!

ACROSS
1 Line of people (5)
3 Pen where pigs are kept (3)
6 Climbing plant (3)
7 Celebration (5)
9 Touching of lips (4)
11 Military body (4)
13 Henry ---, actor (5)
14 Film, --- in Black (3)
15 Tint used on hair (3)
16 Court case (5)

DOWN
1 Fast (5)
4 Native American emblem (5)
5 Type of parrot (5)
8 Incidental remark (5)
10 Tusk material (5)
12 Barbara Streisand film (5)

CROSSWORD a Day!

ACROSS
1 Computer operator (4)
4 Hay storage building (4)
7 Type of pistol (9)
8 Australian lake (4)
10 Grain for sowing (4)
12 Summer seat (9)
13 Shared bedroom (4)
14 Climax (4)

DOWN
2 Charge, sortie (5)
3 Extent (5)
5 Cropped up (5)
6 Unclothed (5)
8 Stopped (5)
9 Speed competitor (5)
10 Neutral vowel sound (5)
11 Cream, pick (5)

CROSSWORD a Day!

ACROSS

1 Gospel (4)
3 Gospel (4)
6 Belly button (5)
7 Drinks cooler? (3)
8 Gospel (7)
13 *10 Things I Hate About* ---, film (3)
14 Musical (5)
15 At any time (4)
16 Gospel (4)

DOWN

1 Brain (4)
2 Genuflected (5)
4 Oily fruit! (5)
5 Require (4)
9 Deep sky blue (5)
10 Slum home (5)
11 *Jane* ---, novel (4)
12 Cad, bounder (4)

LAGOON BOOKS

DAY 23

CROSSWORD a Day!

ACROSS

1 Marina boat (5)
4 Menagerie (3)
5 Meetings (8)
7 Finished (4)
8 Heroic story (4)
11 Animal (8)
13 Slide down snow (3)
14 Loop for trapping (5)

DOWN

1 Beatles album, --- *Submarine* (6)
2 Yearn for (5)
3 Hardy novel, --- *of the D'Urbevilles* (4)
4 Japanese Buddhism (3)
6 Prolonged fight (6)
9 The ---, siege site (5)
10 TV series, --- *City* (4)
12 Hawaiian garland (3)

CROSSWORD a Day!

ACROSS
3 Long country (5)
6 Inuit house? (5)
7 Nude (5)
8 Foolish (7)
12 Italian port (5)
14 Person skilled in a martial art of stealth and camouflage (5)
15 African country (5)

DOWN
1 Locate (4)
2 Beg (5)
3 Non-vowel (9)
4 Writing fluid (3)
5 Small whirlpool (4)
9 Cake topping (5)
10 Man-eating giant (4)
11 Terror (4)
13 No vote (3)

CROSSWORD
a Day!

ACROSS

1. Disney film (5)
4. Affirmative (3)
6 & 17A & 20A. Tolstoy novel (3,3,5)
8. Zesty (5)
12. Avoid (4)
13. Instrument part (4)
14. Autumn fruit (5)
17. See 6A
19. Belly (3)
20. See 6A

DOWN

1. Morning moisture (3)
2. Detract from (3)
3. Film, --- of Africa (3)
4. Japanese money (3)
5. Utter (3)
7. Surviving (5)
9. Measure of land (4)
10. Grassy hue (5)
11. Employer (4)
14. Tom Hanks film (3)
15. Deep track (3)
16. Bark (3)
17. Ottoman commander (3)
18. Outstanding (3)

CROSSWORD a Day!

ACROSS
1 Largest continent (4)
3 Boast (4)
7 Build-up to lift-off (9)
8 Soar (3)
10 Item of clothing (3)
12 TV series with Edward Woodward, *The ---* (9)
13 Quentin Tarantino film, *Reservoir ---*, (4)
14 Sacred (4)

DOWN
2 Go off (5)
4 Perch overnight (5)
5 Spirit from a bottle (5)
6 Infertile (7)
8 Father of psychoanalysis! (5)
9 Offspring (5)
11 Perfect (5)

CROSSWORD
a Day!

ACROSS
1 Venezuelan currency unit (7)
6 Yolk-rich (4)
8 --- *Lies*, film (4)
11 Church instrument (5)
12 Jezebel (4)
14 Shellfish (4)
15 Malaysian currency unit (7)

DOWN
2 Non-clerical (3)
3 Huge tub (3)
4 Brazilian currency unit (7)
5 Swiss currency unit (7)
7 Brush (a horse) (5)
9 Of the kidneys (5)
10 Years of life (3)
13 Cooking pot (3)
14 Mechanical part (3)

CROSSWORD
a Day!

ACROSS

1 Way of approaching a problem (5)
3 Top card (3)
6 Item of footwear (4)
7 Seep out (4)
8 Type of quilt (9)
13 Wise old man (4)
14 Refuse to admit (4)
15 Sleeping place (3)
16 *Point* ---, Keanu Reeves film (5)

DOWN

1 Fable teller (5)
2 Be smug (5)
4 Seat (5)
5 Talon (4)
9 Conscious (5)
10 Head cook (4)
11 Fat (5)
12 Type of canoe (5)

CROSSWORD
a Day!

ACROSS

1 Torso (5)
5 *Kill* ---, film (4)
8 Yell (6)
9 Country, --- Salvador (2)
11 Look! (2)
12 Potato disease (6)
14 Accepted (4)
15 Lewd (5)

DOWN

2 John Candy film, --- *Buck* (5)
3 Part of a shark seen above water (3)
4 Wail (7)
6 Talent (7)
7 Christmas plant (5)
10 Incandescent (5)
13 Vulpine animal (3)

LAGOON BOOKS

CROSSWORD
a Day!

ACROSS
1 Location (8)
6 Hungarian capital (8)
8 Keep out of sight (4)
9 Woodwind instrument (4)
12 Calls out (8)
14 Blue gem (8)

DOWN
2 Animal with ten limbs (5)
3 Reddish wood (4)
4 Dedicated poem (3)
5 Hard metal (5)
7 Animated film about a lovable ogre (5)
10 Animated film about a fawn (5)
11 Freshwater fish (4)
13 American security organization (1,1,1)

CROSSWORD
a Day!

ACROSS
1 See 3D
6 Sibilate (4)
8 Look for (4)
11 Farewell (5)
12 See (4)
14 Heroic poem (4)
15 Characters (7)

DOWN
2 Hydrogen, eg (3)
3 & 1A City
   of Angels (3,7)
4 Room (7)
5 Take illegal control
   of an aircraft (7)
7 Pointed (5)
9 Fit out (5)
10 Leg joint (3)
13 Sweet potato (3)
14 Self-esteem (3)

CROSSWORD
a Day!

ACROSS
1 Jaunty (4)
3 Exchange (4)
7 Bullfighter (8)
9 Make a mistake (3)
10 Inflexible (7)
13 Period (3)
14 Souse (7)
15 Sea movement (4)
16 Vow (4)

DOWN
2 Plus (5)
4 Extended (7)
5 Recreational land (4)
6 Piece (7)
8 Commanded (7)
11 Indulgence (5)
12 Flake of soot (4)

CROSSWORD
a Day!

ACROSS

1 *The --- Family*, 1970s series (9)
6 Rocky (5)
7 Similar (4)
9 Weird (5)
10 Send letter (4)
12 Grin (5)
13 King of Spain, 1474-1516 (9)

DOWN

2 Book of the Bible (4)
3 Underground passage (6)
4 Male duck (5)
5 Black wood (5)
7 Pilot (6)
8 Small blue Belgian! (5)
9 Species of duck (5)
11 Tribe (4)

SOLUTION FOR DAY 32

Across 1. Pert 3. Swap 7. Toreador 9. Era 10. Err 13. Adamant 14. Marinade 15. Tide 16. Oath **Down** 2. Extra 4. Widened 5. Park 6. Segment 8. Ordered 11. Treat 12. Smut

DAY 34

CROSSWORD
a Day!

ACROSS
1. Root (6)
6. Move very slowly (4)
7. Affectionate (6)
9. Heavenly (9)
11. City in Nigeria (6)
12. Midday (4)
13. Number of lords-a-leaping (6)

DOWN
2. Greek island (6)
3. Set principle to follow (9)
4. Bad dream (9)
5. Timid (3)
8. Destroy (6)
10. No matter which (3)

CROSSWORD
a Day!

ACROSS
3 Clean abrasively (5)
6 Level of authority (4)
7 Renown (5)
8 Indicated agreement (6)
10 Sultanate on Borneo (6)
11 Gain a point (5)
12 Type of average (4)
13 Last Greek letter (5)

DOWN
1 San ---, US city (9)
2 Sneering (5)
4 Chilly (4)
5 Beau (9)
7 Literary style (5)
9 Beneath (5)
10 Type of ship (4)

DAY 36

CROSSWORD
a Day!

ACROSS
5 Faulty (9)
7 Rubbed out (6)
9 Swimming costume (6)
12 Australian city (9)

DOWN
1 Appendix (8)
2 Entrails (5)
3 Dull pain (4)
4 Combine (3)
6 Assessor (8)
8 Appointment book (5)
10 Icon (4)
11 Insect (3)

DAY 37

CROSSWORD a Day!

ACROSS
1 Timepiece (5)
5 --- Heche, actress (4)
6 Exterior (5)
8 Remove strength from (6)
10 Rabbits' burrow (6)
12 Knight's weapon (5)
13 Went by horse (4)
14 Samuel ---, famous diarist (5)

DOWN
1 This puzzle! (9)
2 Masticate (4)
3 Serpent (5)
4 Broke (9)
7 James Dean film, --- *Without a Cause* (5)
9 Jane Austen novel, --- *and Prejudice* (5)
11 Moniker (4)

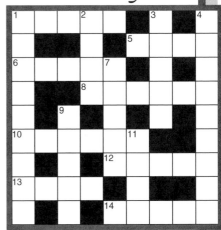

DAY 38

CROSSWORD a Day!

ACROSS

3 Fatigue (4)
5 Separate grain (6)
6 Babble (4)
7 Elvis' home (9)
10 Muslim ascetic (4)
11 Elaborate (6)
12 Viewed (4)

DOWN

1 Scorpion's weapon (5)
2 Melancholy (9)
3 Exciting (9)
4 Black bird (5)
8 Course (5)
9 Stupefied (5)

CROSSWORD
a Day!

ACROSS
1 Type of parrot (5)
6 Monk's attire (5)
7 Mother-of-pearl (5)
8 Leather strip (5)
9 Indian term of respect (5)
12 Run off secretly (5)
13 Species (5)
14 Predilection (5)

DOWN
1 Repair (4)
2 Din (9)
3 Sharpen by rubbing (4)
4 Offensive (9)
5 Male deer (4)
9 Indication (4)
10 Get the better of (4)
11 In this place (4)

CROSSWORD
a Day!

ACROSS
4 Irritate (3)
6 Unit of length (6)
7 Dawdler (9)
10 John ---, writer (9)
12 Constantly (6)
13 Appropriate (3)

DOWN
1 Entertains (6)
2 Amass (6)
3 In a yearning manner (9)
5 Flower (4)
8 Room (6)
9 Dashing (6)
11 Journey (4)

CROSSWORD
a Day!

ACROSS
1 Select (4)
4 Leader of prayers in a mosque (4)
7 Twin-hulled boat (9)
8 Fizzy drink (4)
10 Ran away (4)
12 Unseen, hidden (9)
13 James --- Jones, actor (4)
14 Appointment (4)

DOWN
2 US state (5)
3 Marsupial (5)
5 Painting on a wall (5)
6 Dug out (minerals) from the ground (5)
8 Felony (5)
9 Organ (5)
10 Cooked in oil (5)
11 Red Sea resort (5)

DAY 42

CROSSWORD a Day!

ACROSS
1 Large hill (8)
5 Chart (3)
6 Crave (5)
7 Tend (4)
9 Sturdy vehicle (4)
13 Nimble (5)
14 Lively dance (3)
15 Reckless person (8)

DOWN
1 Impersonator (5)
2 Higher (5)
3 Consideration (4)
4 Female relative (5)
8 Anxiety (5)
10 Hinge joint (5)
11 Young dog (5)
12 Tolerate (4)

DAY 43

CROSSWORD a Day!

ACROSS
1 Kernel (3)
3 Side of a river (4)
5 French capital (5)
6 Insect (3)
8 Once --- a time, fairytale opening (4)
9 Outward shape (4)
11 Electric fish? (3)
13 Lift up (5)
14 Shoreline inlet (5)
15 Marilyn Monroe film, *Some Like It ---* (3)

DOWN
1 Eighth planet (7)
2 Strife, unrest (7)
3 41st US President (4)
4 Barbie's boyfriend (3)
6 Get rid of (7)
7 Storm (7)
10 Hike (4)
12 Facial feature (3)

DAY 44

CROSSWORD
a Day!

ACROSS
1 Self-satisfied (4)
3 Ado (4)
7 Item with which to kill vampires (5)
8 In the past (3)
9 Seabed vessel (9)
12 Used to be (3)
13 Treatise (5)
14 Gollum's precious (4)
15 Retain (4)

DOWN
2 Sports game (5)
4 Utility (5)
5 Stun (5)
6 In the middle of (7)
9 Drain (5)
10 Norwegian playwright (5)
11 Chevy ---, comic actor (5)

CROSSWORD
a Day!

ACROSS

1 Boulder (4)
3 Couch (4)
7 Worth (5)
8 Eisenhower! (3)
9 Biodegrade (3)
10 Yoko ---, artist (3)
11 In what way (3)
13 Feather scarf (3)
14 Foe (5)
15 Jazz pianist,
   --- Ellington (4)
16 Wife of Zeus (4)

DOWN

1 Folk hero (5,4)
2 Troglodyte's home (4)
4 Above (4)
5 Country (9)
6 Ransack (7)
12 Seven days (4)
13 Cowshed (4)

CROSSWORD
a Day!

ACROSS
1 *Meet Joe ---,* Brad Pitt film (5)
6 Country (5)
7 WW1 Antipodean Soldier (5)
9 Precious metal (4)
10 Garish (4)
14 Row of bushes (5)
15 Part of a play (5)
16 Twelve (5)

DOWN
2 English capital (6)
3 Strike with the foot (4)
4 Bizarre (3)
5 Hand over money (for something) (3)
8 Tropical area (6)
11 Lose hair or skin (4)
12 Fire remains (3)
13 Plead (3)

CROSSWORD
a Day!

ACROSS
1 Flying toy (4)
5 Greta ---, film star (5)
7 Monstrosity (7)
8 Miraculous (7)
11 Celestial event (7)
13 South ---, country (5)
14 First man? (4)

DOWN
1 Enthusiastic (4)
2 Adolescent (8)
3 Blade (3)
4 Baby horse (4)
5 Mountain ape (7)
6 Overhauled (8)
9 Cook in the oven (4)
10 Join between two pieces of cloth (4)
12 Business head (1,1,1)

CROSSWORD
a Day!

ACROSS
1 The Big Apple (3,4)
6 Diluted perfume, --- de toilette (3)
7 Concision (7)
8 Cipher (4)
9 *Star Wars* princess (4)
12 Spooky (7)
14 Actress, --- Farrow (3)
15 Sewing tools (7)

DOWN
1 Pen tip (3)
2 Brandish (5)
3 American state (4)
4 Tool to unlock a door (3)
5 Fruit (5)
8 Ring, bong (5)
10 Praise (5)
11 *Star Wars* hero (4)
12 *Star Wars* hero (3)
13 Film, --- *Boot* (3)

CROSSWORD
a Day!

ACROSS
1 You and I (2)
2 Go on an ice rink (5)
7 The --- days, former times (5)
8 Fury (3)
9 Desire (4)
10 Falling flakes? (4)
12 Fusion music (3)
13 Gustav ---, composer (5)
14 The ---, 1960s band (5)
15 Else (2)

DOWN
1 Timber-crafted items (8)
3 Clark ---, Superman (4)
4 Three-sided polygon (8)
5 Individuality (8)
6 Brine (8)
11 African country (4)

DAY 50

CROSSWORD
a Day!

ACROSS
- 2 Bicker (7)
- 5 *Sex and the City* character (9)
- 7 Recluse (5)
- 12 Horticulture (9)
- 14 In a brisk tempo (7)

DOWN
- 1 Fortunate (5)
- 2 Game bird (5)
- 3 Afflict (3)
- 4 Tree creatures from *The Lord of the Rings* (4)
- 6 Be in debt to (3)
- 8 Ancient (3)
- 9 Horned animal (5)
- 10 Heavenly being (5)
- 11 Drag (4)
- 13 Unit of work or energy (3)

CROSSWORD a Day!

ACROSS
1 Hit with the fist (5)
3 Bashful (3)
6 Petroleum (3)
7 --- Carter, Former US President, (5)
9 Deadly contest (4)
11 Injured (4)
13 Change (5)
14 Limb (3)
15 --- Garfunkel, singer (3)
16 Play, --- *Pan* (5)

DOWN
1 Puffed-up (5)
4 *The Simpsons'* dad (5)
5 Illumination (5)
8 Incline (5)
10 Part of a cow (5)
12 Asian feline (5)

CROSSWORD
a Day!

ACROSS
1 Person in a novel (9)
6 Went up in smoke (5)
7 *Barbara* ---, hit for The Beach Boys (3)
8 Dutch cheese (4)
10 Was familiar with (4)
13 Smallest Indian state (3)
14 Spiral (5)
15 Octopus arms (9)

DOWN
2 Type of dog (5)
3 Highest adult male singing voice (4)
4 Track vehicle (5)
5 Regenerate (5)
8 Rowing crew (5)
9 --- Delon, actor (5)
11 Best (5)
12 Flightless bird (4)

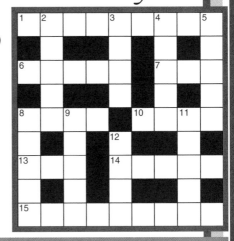

CROSSWORD
a Day!

ACROSS
1 & 3A Oriental room arrangement (4,4)
3 See 1A
7 Imaginary (9)
8 Cash outlet (1,1,1)
10 & 14A Beatles song (3,4)
12 Modern calendar (9)
13 Remainder (4)
14 See 10A

DOWN
2 Throw out (5)
4 Suspicion (5)
5 Piece of wood in another (5)
6 Film, ---: Impossible (7)
8 Bode (5)
9 Mike ---, actor (5)
11 Large antelope (5)

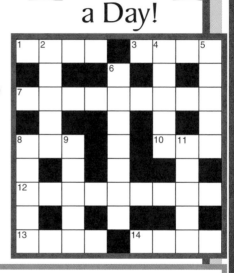

DAY 54

CROSSWORD a Day!

ACROSS

1 First appearance (5)
4 Place (3)
5 Distinctive sight (8)
7 Soon (4)
8 Uninhibited (4)
11 Sleeplessness (8)
13 Observed (3)
14 Ticklish (5)

DOWN

1 1980s TV series about oil tycoons (6)
2 Musical instrument (5)
3 Duration (4)
4 Expected golf score (3)
6 Furtive (6)
9 Film, --- *Room* (5)
10 Mongolian desert (4)
12 Original (3)

SOLUTION FOR DAY 53

Across 1. Feng 3. Shui 7. Fictional 8. ATM 10. Hey 12. Gregorian 13. Rest 14. Jude
Down 2. Evict 4. Hunch 5. Inlay 6. *Mission* 8. Augur 9. Myers 11. Eland

CROSSWORD
a Day!

ACROSS
3 Foreword (5)
6 Actor, --- Atkinson (5)
7 Solid ground, --- firma (5)
8 *The Scorpion King* actor (3,4)
12 Bishop's headwear (5)
14 Puree, mixture (5)
15 Acknowledge (5)

DOWN
1 Get bigger (4)
2 Flooded (5)
3 Head off (9)
4 Bitumen (3)
5 Gemstone (4)
9 Abyss (5)
10 Urban pollution (4)
11 Killed – a dragon? (4)
13 Starting point for a hole of golf (3)

CROSSWORD
a Day!

ACROSS

1 Animal (5)
4 Australian bird (3)
6 Forty winks (3)
8 Ordinary (5)
12 Heap (4)
13 *8 ---*, film (4)
14 Marx brother (5)
17 Unit of electrical current (3)
19 Touch gently, dab (3)
20 Small hill (5)

DOWN

1 Play on words (3)
2 Pinch (3)
3 Snake (3)
4 Greek letter (3)
5 Ancient vase (3)
7 Nimble (5)
9 Baby sheep (4)
10 Middle Eastern religion (5)
11 Seaweed (4)
14 Shoot with a laser gun (3)
15 Companion animal (3)
16 Sturdy tree (3)
17 *Much --- About Nothing*, Shakespeare play (3)
18 Friend (3)

DAY 57

CROSSWORD a Day!

ACROSS
1 Bluish-green (4)
3 Unit of measurement (4)
7 Month (9)
8 Finale (3)
10 Relaxed, sloppy (3)
12 & (9)
13 Irish songstress (4)
14 --- Barrymore, *50 First Dates* actress (4)

DOWN
2 Female monarch (5)
4 Founder of prizes, Alfred --- (5)
5 Small animal (5)
6 First planet (7)
8 Delete (5)
9 One of the Seven Dwarfs (5)
11 Orphan musical (5)

DAY 58

CROSSWORD
a Day!

ACROSS
1 Check carefully (4)
3 Saliva sample (4)
7 Unspoken (5)
8 Holy sister (3)
9 Cambodian capital (5,4)
12 Unit of resistance (3)
13 Quick, lively (5)
14 Reverberation (4)
15 Film, *The --- from Brazil* (4)

DOWN
2 Collision (5)
4 Shrink back in pain (5)
5 Group of bananas (5)
6 Make a list of (7)
9 Show to be true (5)
10 Immature insect (5)
11 Cool (5)

CROSSWORD a Day!

ACROSS
1 Card game (5)
3 Cold (3)
6 Uncommon (4)
7 Roman poet (4)
8 Beneficial feature (9)
13 Falling water (4)
14 Mirth (4)
15 Exercise club (3)
16 Bride's payment (5)

DOWN
1 Type of ham (5)
2 St. Petersburg ballet (5)
4 Stick to (5)
5 Defended building (4)
9 Journal (5)
10 Parent's sister (4)
11 Let (5)
12 Song of lament (5)

CROSSWORD a Day!

ACROSS
1 Writing material (5)
5 Aromatic ointment (4)
8 Relax (6)
9 In such a way (2)
11 *Let It* ---, Beatles song (2)
12 Cavort (6)
14 Servant (4)
15 Vogue (5)

DOWN
2 Conclusive evidence (5)
3 Tree juice (3)
4 Authorize (7)
6 Film and song, *Sweet Home* --- (7)
7 Facial hair (5)
10 Leg joint (5)
13 That man (3)

DAY 61

CROSSWORD a Day!

ACROSS
1 Caribbean island (8)
6 Caribbean island (8)
8 Semi-precious stone (4)
9 Please reply (1,1,1,1)
12 Deftly (8)
14 Caribbean island (8)

DOWN
2 Wryness (5)
3 Judi Dench film (4)
4 Arabian tale, --- *Baba and the Forty Thieves* (3)
5 Marx brother (5)
7 Arctic or Antarctic (5)
10 Substantial (5)
11 An arm or a leg? (4)
13 Long narrow inlet (3)

LAGOON BOOKS

CROSSWORD
a Day!

ACROSS
1 Root vegetable (7)
6 Implement for detangling hair (4)
8 Pinion (4)
11 Improper (5)
12 Bohemian (4)
14 On (4)
15 The Flintstone's daughter (7)

DOWN
2 Massage (3)
3 At present (3)
4 Outrage (7)
5 Breakfast receptacles? (7)
7 Scale (5)
9 Useless (5)
10 Computer screen (1,1,1)
13 Lout (3)
14 Small tool (3)

CROSSWORD
a Day!

ACROSS

1 Social gathering (5)
4 Obese (3)
6 Type of metal (3)
8 Look after (5)
12 Perimeter (4)
13 Developed (4)
14 Ward off a weapon (5)
17 Choose (3)
19 Running bill (3)
20 Below (5)

DOWN

1 Plant container (3)
2 Flee (3)
3 Japanese currency (3)
4 In support of (3)
5 Digit (3)
7 Country in Asia (5)
9 Compulsion (4)
10 Woolly animal (5)
11 Will's beneficiary (4)
14 Large hole (3)
15 Chest bone (3)
16 Film, *Stuck On ---* (3)
17 Elderly (3)
18 Road material (3)

CROSSWORD
a Day!

ACROSS
1 Fictional spy (5,4)
6 Cash (5)
7 Musical group (4)
9 Luciano Pavarotti, eg (5)
10 Satellite (4)
12 --- *Lane*, Beatles song (5)
13 1A film (9)

DOWN
2 Expectantly (4)
3 Soccer team (6)
4 Academy award (5)
5 Fop (5)
7 Anne ---, Henry VIII's second wife (6)
8 Prime Minister: 'first --- equals' (5)
9 Piece of absorbent fabric (5)
11 Be jealous of (4)

DAY 65

CROSSWORD
a Day!

ACROSS
1 False (6)
6 Annoy 4)
7 Type of architecture (6)
9 Tactical (9)
11 Leash (6)
12 Wealthy (4)
13 Annually (6)

DOWN
2 Snobbish (6)
3 Sick (9)
4 Group of musicians (9)
5 Aircraft (3)
8 Resembling a pine cone (6)
10 Snoop (3)

CROSSWORD
a Day!

ACROSS
3 Scrap of food (5)
6 Bird of peace (4)
7 Breathe noisily when asleep (5)
8 Insect (6)
10 Salad ingredient (6)
11 Alliance (5)
12 Hereditary unit (4)
13 Bird that catches the worm (5)

DOWN
1 Jaunt, quest (9)
2 Prevent (5)
4 Step of a ladder (4)
5 *Eroica* composer (9)
7 Carly ---, *You're So Vain* singer (5)
9 Nut-bearing tree (5)
10 Charge to use a road (4)

CROSSWORD
a Day!

ACROSS
5 Fictitious name (9)
7 Salary (6)
9 Malaysian garment (6)
12 Book lender (9)

DOWN
1 Discretionary (8)
2 Barrier (5)
3 Dutch cheese (4)
4 African antelope (3)
6 Hard wood (8)
8 Red-breasted bird (5)
10 Slightly open (4)
11 US security agency (3)

CROSSWORD a Day!

ACROSS
1 Wine ingredient (5)
5 Actor, --- Curtis (4)
6 Third planet (5)
8 See 2D
10 & 13A Lynn Redgrave film (6,4)
12 Underside of a projecting roof (5)
13 See 10A
14 Painter of ballet dancers (5)

DOWN
1 Fruit (9)
2 & 8A Colonial headwear (4,6)
3 Ideology (5)
4 Coalescence (9)
7 Safeguard (bets) (5)
9 Contrite (5)
11 Ivy League university (4)

DAY 69

CROSSWORD a Day!

ACROSS
3 Roguish, cheeky (4)
5 Persuaded (6)
6 Arm bone (4)
7 Bearable (9)
10 Continent (4)
11 Strip of pasta (6)
12 Let it stand (4)

DOWN
1 Dash (5)
2 Bubbly (9)
3 Worship (9)
4 Man-made waterway (5)
8 Beginning (5)
9 Stand out (5)

DAY 70

CROSSWORD a Day!

ACROSS
1 *Planet of the ---*, sci-fi film (4)
4 Stylish (4)
7 & 10D Drink (9,5)
8 Those people (4)
10 Joke (4)
12 Able to be split (9)
13 Oxidization (4)
14 Tips (4)

DOWN
2 Become hot and dry (5)
3 --- Lyle, golfer (5)
5 Gang, swarm (5)
6 Church vault (5)
8 English royal house (5)
9 The King (5)
10 See 7A
11 Substantial, firm (5)

CROSSWORD
a Day!

ACROSS
4 Combine (3)
6 Legendary female warrior (6)
7 Prickly animal (9)
10 Can be turned around (9)
12 Weak (6)
13 Definite article (3)

DOWN
1 Mollycoddle (6)
2 Vegetable (6)
3 Step forward (9)
5 Sunrise (4)
8 Drink (6)
9 Small hole (in shoes) (6)
11 Solemn promise (4)

LAGOON
BOOKS

DAY 72

CROSSWORD
a Day!

ACROSS
1 Actor, --- Sharif (4)
4 Source of power (4)
7 Amusement (9)
8 Turquoise (4)
10 *King* ---, play (4)
12 New York island (9)
13 Robin Williams film (4)
14 Compass point (4)

DOWN
2 Actress, --- Ringwald (5)
3 Manmade material (5)
5 Join together (5)
6 European beer (5)
8 Heavenly body (5)
9 Ruffle (5)
10 Machine for shaping wood (5)
11 Bryan ---, singer (5)

CROSSWORD a Day!

ACROSS
3 Children's nurse (5)
6 Perplexed (2,3)
7 Sailors' lure (5)
8 Personal (7)
12 Insurgent (5)
14 Madagascan animal (5)
15 Mark (5)

DOWN
1 Candle-like (4)
2 Michaelmas daisy (5)
3 Country music city (9)
4 And not (3)
5 Jerk (4)
9 Actor, --- Lee Jones (5)
10 Rum and water (4)
11 Ripped (4)
13 --- constrictor, snake (3)

CROSSWORD a Day!

ACROSS
1 Eucalyptus, --- tree (3)
3 Fruit (4)
5 Cleanse (5)
6 *Catcher in the ---,* seminal novel (3)
8 Adjoin, --- on (4)
9 Number (4)
11 By now (3)
13 Musical form (5)
14 Jolly (5)
15 Tibetan ox (3)

DOWN
1 Teutonic country (7)
2 Search for a felon (7)
3 Promenade (4)
4 Month (3)
6 Penguin colony (7)
7 Set aside (7)
10 Small horse (4)
12 Survive, --- out (3)

LAGOON BOOKS

DAY 75

CROSSWORD
a Day!

ACROSS
1 Wild goat (4)
3 Wading bird (4)
7 Breadmaker (5)
8 Zero score (3)
9 Unusual largeness (9)
12 Nelson Mandela's party (1,1,1)
13 Mistake (5)
14 Céline ---, singer (4)
15 Place to wash (4)

DOWN
2 Indian delicacy (5)
4 Sydney beach (5)
5 Location of the 1692 witch hunt (5)
6 Trifling ornament (7)
9 Great, showy (5)
10 Lizard (5)
11 Fire (a gun) (5)

CROSSWORD a Day!

ACROSS
1 Fourth planet (4)
3 Breeding farm (4)
7 Charlie ---, actor (5)
8 Tool for turning soil (3)
9 Graveyard tree (3)
10 Stale (3)
11 Michael Jordan's league (3)
13 Tin receptacle (3)
14 Oklahoma city (5)
15 Wordless act (4)
16 Tiller (4)

DOWN
1 Machine part (9)
2 Romantic flower (4)
4 Miniscule (4)
5 Evolution theory (9)
6 Group of guys (7)
12 Small particle (4)
13 Arrived (4)

CROSSWORD
a Day!

ACROSS
1 Rotate (4)
3 Whitish metal (4)
7 Film, --- of
 the Hunter (5)
8 Oil platform (3)
9 Pose (a question) (3)
10 Pigpen (3)
11 Whiskey shot (3)
13 Simon Le ---, Duran
 Duran singer (3)
14 Picture stand (5)
15 Michael ---, actor (4)
16 Latest events (4)

DOWN
1 Land (9)
2 Telephoned (4)
4 Tiny amount (4)
5 Arrogance (9)
6 Self-centeredness (7)
12 Sign of sorrow (4)
13 Once in a
 --- moon, rarely (4)

CROSSWORD
a Day!

ACROSS
1 Bloke (4)
5 Fire-starting (5)
7 Arc in the sky (7)
8 Florida beach (7)
11 Embodiment (7)
13 Weighed down (5)
14 Taj Mahal city (4)

DOWN
1 Central part (4)
2 Lively (8)
3 Advantage (3)
4 Wear away by biting (4)
5 Opt to not vote (7)
6 Last performance (8)
9 Christian ---, actor (4)
10 Brightest star in Lyra constellation (4)
12 For each (3)

CROSSWORD
a Day!

ACROSS
1 Pagan (7)
6 A single thing (3)
7 Tailless pet (4,3)
8 Protein-rich bean (4)
9 Blotch (4)
12 Row of houses (7)
14 Grief (3)
15 Improve (7)

DOWN
1 That man (3)
2 Irritate (5)
3 German wine (4)
4 Bond film, *The World Is --- Enough* (3)
5 Storehouse (5)
6 Tintin's dog (5)
10 Ordinary (5)
11 Roman doorway (4)
12 Golf peg (3)
13 Day before (3)

CROSSWORD
a Day!

ACROSS
1 Carry out (2)
2 Diagram (5)
7 Frightening fish (5)
8 Knight's title (3)
9 Arena for skating (4)
10 Ferment (4)
12 Animation technique (1,1,1)
13 Stretchy material (5)
14 Banded mineral (5)
15 All right (1,1)

DOWN
1 Administrative area (8)
3 Walk in the hills (4)
4 Limit (8)
5 Picture in oils (8)
6 Impairment (8)
11 Hole for putting coins through (4)

CROSSWORD
a Day!

ACROSS
- 2 Dry white Burgundy (7)
- 5 Disintegration (9)
- 7 Factory (5)
- 12 Diplodocus and stegasaurus, eg (9)
- 14 Container in which to wash (7)

DOWN
- 1 Book for photos (5)
- 2 Inexpensive (5)
- 3 Pose a query (3)
- 4 American state (4)
- 6 Put on (clothes) (3)
- 8 Star sign (3)
- 9 Opposable finger (5)
- 10 Thing of value (5)
- 11 Singer, --- Turner (4)
- 13 Collection of related items (3)

CROSSWORD
a Day!

ACROSS
1 Board game (5)
3 Song, --- Maria (3)
6 --- dwarf, old star (3)
7 Country (5)
9 Journey (4)
11 Worry (4)
13 Cord, band (5)
14 See 15A
15 & 14A Nicolas Cage film (3,3)
16 Spring-lock (5)

DOWN
1 Measure of gold (5)
4 Device for controlling flow (5)
5 Employees (5)
8 Sprig of small flowers (5)
10 Proportion (5)
12 Portable lamp (5)

DAY 83

CROSSWORD a Day!

ACROSS

1 Drop (into) (9)
6 Escort (5)
7 Label (3)
8 Kiss on the cheek (4)
10 Character from Uncle Remus , --- Rabbit (4)
13 Alias (1,1,1)
14 *Starsky and Hutch* character, --- Bear (5)
15 Song, --- *Over The Rainbow* (9)

DOWN

2 Walkway (5)
3 Actor, --- Grant (4)
4 Absolute (5)
5 Keen (5)
8 *Twin ---*, cult series (5)
9 Charisma (5)
11 --- Allan Poe, writer (5)
12 Display (4)

CROSSWORD
a Day!

ACROSS
- 1 Repair (4)
- 3 Zealous (4)
- 6 Incantation (5)
- 7 Born as (3)
- 8 Dustin Hoffman film (4,3)
- 13 Jump on one leg (3)
- 14 Anne Brontë novel, --- *Grey* (5)
- 15 Harmony (4)
- 16 Small piece of a hard material (4)

DOWN
- 1 The majority of (4)
- 2 Indian capital (5)
- 4 *Uncle* ---, play (5)
- 5 Animal (4)
- 9 Ski resort (5)
- 10 Witchcraft (5)
- 11 Chance (4)
- 12 Pronto! (1,1,1,1)

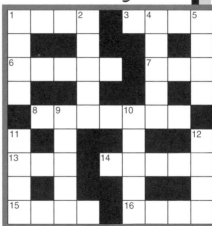

CROSSWORD
a Day!

ACROSS
1 Robber (5)
4 Horizontal line (3)
5 Faith, creed (8)
7 See 9D
8 *Born Free* lioness (4)
11 Divert (8)
13 Lemon seed (3)
14 *The --- Bunch*, 1970s series (5)

DOWN
1 Sikh headwear (6)
2 Islands (5)
3 Phileas ---, fictional globetrotter (4)
4 Brazilian city (3)
6 Larder (6)
9 & 7A Tibetan dog (5,4)
10 Knife (4)
12 Sprite (3)

CROSSWORD a Day!

ACROSS
3 Robbery (5)
6 Got up (5)
7 Substance used in bread-making (5)
8 & 13D & 14A TV series and film (7,3,5)
12 Slender crown (5)
14 See 8A
15 Pattern (5)

DOWN
1 Treaty (4)
2 Site of a trial (5)
3 Thor ---, Kon-Tiki adventurer (9)
4 --- Gershwin, lyricist (3)
5 London art gallery (4)
9 Communal fund (5)
10 Stalk (4)
11 Area of London (4)
13 See 8A

CROSSWORD
a Day!

ACROSS
1 Power (5)
4 Turf (3)
6 Precious stone (3)
8 Poet, --- Dickinson (5)
12 & 13A 1977 film (4)
13 See 12A
14 Publish (5)
17 *Monster* band (1,1,1)
19 Grandma (3)
20 Army rank (5)

DOWN
1 Thick mist (3)
2 Caribbean spirit (3)
3 Female sheep (3)
4 Used on snow (3)
5 24 hours (3)
7 Sign up to participate (5)
9 Cuts (grass) (4)
10 Sizeable (5)
11 Cereal (4)
14 Badge attachment (3)
15 Sir --- McKellen, actor (3)
16 Actor, --- Curry (3)
17 British in colonial India (3)
18 Former space station (3)

SOLUTION FOR DAY 86

Across 3. Heist 6. Arose 7. Yeast 8. Starsky 12. Tiara 14. Hutch 15. Model
Down 1. Pact 2. Court 3. Heyerdahl 4. Ira 5. Tate 9. Kitty 10. Stem 11. Soho 13. And

DAY 88

CROSSWORD a Day!

ACROSS
1 Loot (4)
3 Medicinal plant (4)
7 Annoy (9)
8 Turkish hat (3)
10 Boy (3)
12 Official watchdog (9)
13 Urban transport (4)
14 *Moonstruck* actress (4)

DOWN
2 Bing Crosby hit, --- *Christmas* (5)
4 Modern communication (1-4)
5 Bear offspring (5)
6 American state (7)
8 Ignore (rules) (5)
9 Black-and-white animal (5)
11 Conscious (of something) (5)

LAGOON BOOKS

CROSSWORD
a Day!

ACROSS
- **1** Fairly hot (4)
- **3** Full extent (4)
- **7 & 12D** Actor (8,4)
- **9** Feather scarf (3)
- **10** Singer, --- Cassidy (3)
- **14** Director, --- Howard (3)
- **15** Epidemic (8)
- **16** Portal (4)
- **17** Blackness (4)

DOWN
- **2** Musketeer (5)
- **4** Nuisance (4)
- **5** Not any (4)
- **6** Courage (7)
- **8** Self-help body (1,1)
- **11** Fire prod (5)
- **12** See 7A
- **13** The Iron Chancellor, --- von Bismarck (4)
- **14** Egyptian sun god (2)

CROSSWORD a Day!

ACROSS
1 Brief (5)
3 UK TV company (1,1,1)
6 Stake (4)
7 Peer (4)
8 Henry ---,
   US statesman (9)
13 Musical phrase (4)
14 Infamous
   grave robber (4)
15 British vessel (1,1,1)
16 Hugh ---, actor (5)

DOWN
1 Fiery particle (5)
2 Captain Scott's
   Antarctic colleague (5)
4 Infamous
   grave robber (5)
5 Open pie (4)
9 Saying (5)
10 Gentle (4)
11 African country (5)
12 --- Butler, character in
   Gone With the Wind (5)

CROSSWORD
a Day!

ACROSS
1 Coen brother, filmmaker (5)
5 Coen brother, filmmaker (4)
8 Domed Native American tent (6)
9 In the morning (1,1)
11 Hitler's police (1,1)
12 Human being (6)
14 Humble (4)
15 Albert ---, writer (5)

DOWN
2 Moveable joint (5)
3 Employment (3)
4 Basic unit (7)
6 Amazing (7)
7 Desert animal (5)
10 Sacred song (5)
13 Irritate (3)

DAY 92

CROSSWORD

a Day!

ACROSS

1 Number (8)
6 Pleasantries (8)
8 Look lasciviously (4)
9 Imploring request (4)
12 Independence (8)
14 Meddlesome individual (8)

DOWN

2 Sound (5)
3 Those people (4)
4 Old Testament prophet (3)
5 Chinese or Indonesian, eg (5)
7 Transparent (5)
10 Purgatory (5)
11 Actor, --- Garcia (4)
13 T-shaped (cross) (3)

CROSSWORD
a Day!

ACROSS
1 The Merchant of Venice (7)
6 Actor, --- Alda (4)
8 Burrowing animal (4)
11 Cook in an oven (5)
12 Male (Chinese) (4)
14 Verbal test (4)
15 Give a right (7)

DOWN
2 Female (Chinese) (3)
3 Unit of resistance (3)
4 Character in *M*A*S*H** (7)
5 Type of surgery (7)
7 Television producer, --- Spelling (5)
9 River mammal (5)
10 Levy (3)
13 Intestine (3)
14 Frequently (3)

CROSSWORD
a Day!

ACROSS
1 Edge (4)
3 Adept (4)
7 Control (8)
9 --- Tyler, actress (3)
10 System
(of currency) (7)
13 Racket (3)
14 Appendage (8)
15 Ooze (4)
16 South American
country (4)

DOWN
2 Unfastened (5)
4 Bombast (7)
5 Scrimped (4)
6 Spoil (7)
8 Late (7)
11 Passenger ship (5)
12 Singing voice (4)

CROSSWORD
a Day!

Across
1 Scottish capital (9)
6 Demolish (5)
7 Swerve (4)
9 Mixture of rain and snow (5)
10 Evaluate (4)
12 Type of tea from India (5)
13 Northern English city (9)

Down
2 Hemispherical roof (4)
3 Snuggle (6)
4 Nail for holding metal plates together (5)
5 Beating organ (5)
7 Against (in sport) (6)
8 Clean (feathers) (5)
9 Dried cereal stalks (5)
11 Stone boundary (4)

CROSSWORD a Day!

ACROSS
1 Fastener (3)
3 Throw (a caber) (4)
5 Sonorous element (5)
6 Carry On star, --- James (3)
8 Madame Bovary's first name (4)
9 Just (4)
11 World games organizing body (1,1,1)
13 Branch of Islam (5)
14 Put together (5)
15 Gripe at (3)

DOWN
1 African river (7)
2 Washington DC river (7)
3 Lean (4)
4 Jet ---, water vehicle (3)
6 Irish river (7)
7 Endearing term (7)
10 Habitually did, --- to (4)
12 Antique (3)

DAY 97

CROSSWORD a Day!

ACROSS
3 Gale (5)
6 Empty space (4)
7 Stomach (5)
8 Edible creature (6)
10 International association (6)
11 Prize (5)
12 Old-fashioned instrument (4)
13 Follow (5)

DOWN
1 Cocoa snack (9)
2 Nerve, spirit (5)
4 Affectedly quaint (4)
5 Ship on which the Pilgrims sailed to America (9)
7 Insipid (5)
9 Circulate (5)
10 Asian language (4)

CROSSWORD

a Day!

ACROSS
5 Lively (9)
7 Overrun (6)
9 Ridiculous (6)
12 Patience (9)

DOWN
1 Water deposit (8)
2 Go away (5)
3 Grew old (4)
4 Consumed (3)
6 Dealer in
   ships' supplies (8)
8 Comical (6)
10 Farm building (4)
11 Moose (3)

CROSSWORD a Day!

ACROSS
1 Verse of a poem (5)
3 Film, --- *Age* (3)
6 Animated film about an insect colony (4)
7 Western, --- *Upon a Time in the West* (4)
8 Thousands of years (9)
13 Tablet (4)
14 *The* ---, Jackie Collins novel (4)
15 Conserve (3)
16 Level, tier (5)

DOWN
1 Allegation (5)
2 Of birth (5)
4 Spiky plants (5)
5 *High* ---, Western (4)
9 Balearic island (5)
10 *Run --- Run*, film (4)
11 Dapper (5)
12 Catkins tree (5)

LAGOON BOOKS

DAY 100

CROSSWORD
a Day!

ACROSS
1 Projecting window (5)
4 Actor, --- Holm (3)
5 Bounty mutineer, --- Christian (8)
7 Slope (4)
8 In ---, in its original place (4)
11 New York borough (8)
13 Low insular bank (3)
14 Clean abrasively (5)

DOWN
1 English University (6)
2 Part of the small intestine (5)
3 Fastening device (4)
4 Fury, rage (3)
6 J M W ---, artist (6)
9 Inuit house (5)
10 Company head (4)
12 Rob ---, Scottish hero (3)

CROSSWORD a Day!

ACROSS

1 Fizzy drink (4)
3 Cut into small pieces (4)
6 Hindu God of war (5)
7 Octopus fluid (3)
8 Palm tree fruit (7)
13 Atmosphere (3)
14 Ornamental tower (5)
15 Black eye make-up (4)
16 Czar, --- the Terrible (4)

DOWN

1 Piece of money (4)
2 Georges ---, composer (5)
4 Japanese poem (5)
5 Prod (4)
9 Talk show host, --- Winfrey (5)
10 Supermodel, --- Campbell (5)
11 Cold and musty (4)
12 French city (4)

CROSSWORD
a Day!

ACROSS
- 4 Toupee (3)
- 6 Flippantly (6)
- 7 Doctor (9)
- 10 Diminutive (9)
- 12 Channel (6)
- 13 --- Hur, film (3)

DOWN
- 1 Native American beads (6)
- 2 Drawing tool (6)
- 3 Final demand (9)
- 5 US Hawkeye state (4)
- 8 Lizard (6)
- 9 Goad (6)
- 11 William ---, playwright (4)

CROSSWORD
a Day!

ACROSS
1 Girl (4)
4 Stop (4)
7 Johann --- Bach, composer (9)
8 Valley (4)
10 Tramp (4)
12 Follower of Jesus (9)
13 Use one's eyes (4)
14 Long tube (4)

DOWN
2 Stadium (5)
3 Leftover (5)
5 Friend, comrade (5)
6 Argentine dance (5)
8 Oral (5)
9 One of the Florida Keys (5)
10 Break out of the egg (5)
11 Edible seeds (5)

CROSSWORD
a Day!

ACROSS
1 Italian food (5)
5 Off-white (4)
8 Floor covering (6)
9 Kofi Annan's organization (1,1)
11 Radio broadcaster (1,1)
12 Yell (6)
14 Melody (4)
15 Kingly (5)

DOWN
2 Diminutive (5)
3 No. 1 in cards (3)
4 Patronymic (7)
6 Tartness (7)
7 Sandy area (5)
10 Dame --- Melba, opera singer (5)
13 Writing fluid (3)

DAY 105

ACROSS

1 Quid pro ---, compensation (3)
3 Hint (4)
5 Thespian (5)
6 Dry (wine) (3)
8 Brad Pitt film (4)
9 Group of countries (4)
11 Regret (3)
13 Sour fruit (5)
14 Sweet fruit (5)
15 Negative vote (3)

DOWN

1 Fourth (7)
2 Result (7)
3 Abrupt (4)
4 Before (4)
6 Biblical wise man (7)
7 Londoner! (7)
10 Scheme (4)
12 Employ, utilize (3)

CROSSWORD
a Day!

ACROSS

1 & 3A Tip of South America (4,4)
3 See 1A
7 Well done! (5)
8 Challenge (3)
9 Backpacks (9)
12 Inn (3)
13 Colossal (5)
14 Dorothy's dog in *The Wizard of Oz* (4)
15 Spanish painter (4)

DOWN

2 Protective garment tied at the back (5)
4 Of the eye (5)
5 Network (5)
6 Small bouquet (7)
9 Broken (5)
10 Head monk (5)
11 Sri Lankan city (5)

CROSSWORD
a Day!

ACROSS
1 Actor,--- McGregor (4)
3 Acquiesce (4)
7 Kevin ---, actor (5)
8 Evita, --- Perón (3)
9 Mother's ruin! (3)
10 Snoop (3)
11 --- Robbins, actor (3)
13 High-protein food (3)
14 Straighten up (5)
15 Doh, eg (4)
16 Rugs (4)

DOWN
1 Delight (9)
2 Swedish band (4)
4 Explosion (4)
5 Brat Pack film (5,4)
6 Star sign (7)
12 Ship's post (4)
13 Irish songstress (4)

CROSSWORD
a Day!

ACROSS
1 Goods in store (5)
6 Boudicca's tribe (5)
7 Richard Rountree film (5)
9 Beach crustacean (4)
10 Prayer ending (4)
14 Filled pancake (5)
15 Sign of life (5)
16 Film, --- *Rotten Scoundrels* (5)

DOWN
2 Top (1-5)
3 Bird of prey (4)
4 Stitched edge (3)
5 Facial feature (3)
8 Drink dispenser (6)
11 Covered in sugar (4)
12 Secret agent (3)
13 1980s TV series about an alien (3)

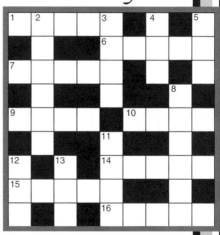

SOLUTION FOR DAY 107

Across 1. Ewan 3. Obey 7. Bacon 8. Eva 9. Gin 10. Pry 11. Tim 13. Egg 14. Align 15 Nate 16. Mats **Down** 1. Entertain 2. ABBA 4. Bang 5. Young Guns 6. Scorpio 12. Mast 13. Enya

CROSSWORD
a Day!

ACROSS
1 Occupy completely (4)
5 Shoreline (5)
7 & 11A Author of *The Jungle Book* (7,7)
8 *Atomic* band (7)
11 See 7A
13 Legal documents (5)
14 Opposed (4)

DOWN
1 Agricultural site (4)
2 Feminine (8)
3 Rocky hill (3)
4 River in Hades (4)
5 Snoozes (7)
6 Extra (8)
9 Go by bicycle (4)
10 Wrinkled fruit (4)
12 Wedding-day promise (1,2)

SOLUTION FOR DAY 108

Across 1. Stock 6. Iceni 7. Shaft 9. Crab 10. Amen 14. Crepe 15. Pulse 16. Dirty
Down 2. T-shirt 3. Kite 4. Hem 5. Lip 8. Teapot 11. Iced 12. Spy 13. ALF.

ACROSS

1 Majestic, august (8)
6 Retrospectively validate (8)
8 Barb (4)
9 T-Rex front man, --- Bolan (4)
12 In a disorderly manner (4-4)
14 Country, capital Kuala Lumpur (8)

DOWN

2 Instrument (5)
3 Garden tool (4)
4 In the style of (1,2)
5 Collect (5)
7 Gaming tokens (5)
10 Book of maps (5)
11 Hostel (1,1,1,1)
13 Meadow (3)

CROSSWORD a Day!

ACROSS
1 *10* star, --- Derek (2)
2 Aroma (5)
7 Piquant jelly (5)
8 Indian bread (3)
9 Actress, --- Winslet (4)
10 Sparkling wine (4)
12 Country (1,1,1)
13 Beatle, --- Starr (5)
14 Bond car, --- Martin (5)
15 Beside (2)

DOWN
1 Loss of electricity (8)
3 A lot of (4)
4 UK landmark at western tip (5,3)
5 Spick and span (8)
6 Blood component (8)
11 Jason's ship (4)

SOLUTION FOR DAY 110

Across 1. Imperial 6. Backdate 8. Hook 9. Marc 12. Pell-mell 14. Malaysia **Down** 2. Piano 3. Rake 4. A la 5. Fetch 7. Chips 10. Atlas 11. YMCA 13. Lea

CROSSWORD
a Day!

ACROSS
2 King --- I, the Lionheart (7)
5 *Top Gun* actor (3,6)
7 Bend down (5)
12 Comedy series with Ricky Gervais (3,6)
14 Celebrity, fame (7)

DOWN
1 Oriental plant (5)
2 *Groundhog Day* director Harold ---, (5)
3 Mangy dog (3)
4 Be in a hurry (4)
6 Spaceship (1,1,1)
8 Also (3)
9 Light-refracting piece of glass (5)
10 Applaud (5)
11 Gossip (4)
13 Passing craze (3)

CROSSWORD
a Day!

ACROSS
1 Director,
 --- Columbus (5)
3 Monitor (1,1,1)
6 Legendary bird (3)
7 Set of warships (5)
9 Attic (4)
11 Unfeeling (4)
13 Shelled animal (5)
14 That woman (3)
15 --- Luthor, nemesis of Superman, (3)
16 Hydrophobic (5)

DOWN
1 Christmas hymn (5)
4 Reverie (5)
5 Board (5)
8 Sedate (5)
10 Unit of measurement (5)
12 Stultified (5)

DAY 114

CROSSWORD a Day!

ACROSS
- **1 & 6A** South Atlantic island (7,2,5)
- **6** See 1A
- **7** Container's top (3)
- **8** Emend (4)
- **10** Code to identify a published work (1,1,1,1)
- **13** Female deer (3)
- **14** Licit (5)
- **15** Novel, --- *Heights* (9)

DOWN
- **2** Circular (5)
- **3** Rip (4)
- **4** Frasier's brother (5)
- **5** Actor, --- Quinn (5)
- **8** Fund (5)
- **9** Sluggish (5)
- **11** Thinking organ (5)
- **12** Elvis hit, --- *Suede Shoes* (4)

CROSSWORD
a Day!

ACROSS
1 Brace (4)
3 Support (4)
6 Rigid (5)
7 Old piece of cloth (3)
8 American state (7)
13 Donkey (3)
14 Oven (5)
15 Murderous barber Sweeney ---, (4)
16 Snare (4)

DOWN
1 Overtake (4)
2 Direct (5)
4 Repeat (5)
5 Leaf (4)
9 Relieved (pain) (5)
10 Eight lines of verse (5)
11 Final (4)
12 Plant from which rope is made (4)

CROSSWORD
a Day!

ACROSS
1 Arrive at (5)
4 & **4D** Leader of the Khmer Rouge (3,3)
5 Set into action (8)
7 Well-ventilated (4)
8 & **13A** & **14A** Comedy series (4,3,5)
11 Suffragette, --- Pankhurst (8)
13 See 8A
14 See 8A

DOWN
1 Ronald ---, 1980s US President (6)
2 Religious block (5)
3 Possess (4)
4 See 4A
6 Claim (6)
9 Balearic island (5)
10 Ice mountain? (4)
12 Wet soil (3)

SOLUTION FOR DAY 115
Across 1. Pair 3. Prop 6. Stiff 7. Rag 8. Vermont 13. Ass 14. Stove 15. Todd 16. Trap
Down 1. Pass 2. Refer 4. Rerun 5. Page 9. Eased 10. Octet 11. Last 12. Hemp

CROSSWORD
a Day!

ACROSS

3 Valuables store (5)
6 Diving bird (5)
7 Stand-in doctor (5)
8 Biased (7)
12 Bit (5)
14 Jumps vertically (horse) (5)
15 Flower (5)

DOWN

1 Composer, --- Stravinsky (4)
2 Ancient ruined city (5)
3 Tinky Winky, eg (9)
4 Fantasy monster (3)
5 Jane Austen novel (4)
9 Character in Wonderland (5)
10 Corrosive liquid (4)
11 Stylish (4)
13 Submachine gun (3)

CROSSWORD a Day!

ACROSS
1 Crude, stupid (5)
4 Top of a cooker (3)
6 Young man (3)
8 Southern African desert (5)
12 Of sound mind (4)
13 Existence (4)
14 Spanish dishes (5)
17 Skill (3)
19 Use a spade (3)
20 Exercise (3-2)

DOWN
1 Taxi (3)
2 Some (3)
3 Breaking of a moral law (3)
4 Mouth a tune (3)
5 Baby's protective cloth (3)
7 Scarlett ---, character in *Gone With the Wind* (1'4)
9 TV series, --- McBeal (4)
10 Imply (5)
11 Greek goat's cheese (4)
14 Bit (3)
15 Lapdog (3)
16 British regiment (1,1,1)
17 Suitable (3)
18 Gratuity (3)

CROSSWORD
a Day!

ACROSS
1. Son in The Simpsons (4)
3. Capital of Norway (4)
6. Brindled (cat) (5)
7. Charles Aznavour song (3)
8. Mythical bird (7)
13. On behalf of (3)
14. Thieved (5)
15. Spool (4)
16. Quiet! (4)

DOWN
1. Each of two (4)
2. Socially prohibited (5)
4. Japanese cuisine (5)
5. Actor, --- Wilson (4)
9. Animal (5)
10. V-shaped cut (5)
11. At a great distance (4)
12. Net (4)

CROSSWORD
a Day!

ACROSS
4 Flightless bird (3)
6 Culmination (6)
7 Uproarious (9)
10 Electrical conductor (9)
12 Polar region (6)
13 Cunning animal? (3)

DOWN
1 --- du Maurier, writer (6)
2 Furniture inlay pattern (6)
3 Region (9)
5 Bill of fare (4)
8 Portuguese city (6)
9 Oral communication (6)
11 Company emblem (4)

CROSSWORD
a Day!

ACROSS
1 Ozzy Osbourne's daughter (5)
3 Towards the stern (3)
6 *Fly --- Home*, film (4)
7 Hop-drying kiln (4)
8 Nepali capital (9)
13 Ozzy Osbourne's son (4)
14 Escaped (4)
15 World Wide Web (3)
16 Reception (5)

DOWN
1 Trick (5)
2 Minimum (5)
4 Melted together (5)
5 Couch (4)
9 Open-mouthed (5)
10 Marine fish (4)
11 Singer, --- Furtado (5)
12 Beneath (5)

DAY 122

CROSSWORD a Day!

ACROSS
1 Six-sided shape (4)
5 Plait (5)
7 Flood (7)
8 Clairvoyant (7)
11 Leslie ---, star of *The Naked Gun* (7)
13 Portents (5)
14 Twelfth of a foot (4)

DOWN
1 Actress, --- Blanchett (4)
2 Dawn chorus? (8)
3 Ashes receptacle (3)
4 Nervous (4)
5 Shorelines (7)
6 Rowan ---, actor (8)
9 In case (4)
10 Egyptian symbol of life (4)
12 *Holiday* ---, film (3)

LAGOON BOOKS

CROSSWORD
a Day!

ACROSS
1 Al Pacino film (8)
6 In the open air (8)
8 Close one eye briefly as a signal (4)
9 Reference: in the same book (4)
12 Countrywide (8)
14 Ocean (8)

DOWN
2 See 5D
3 Sack (4)
4 Type of lettuce (3)
5 & 2D Director (5,5)
7 Music with an easy flowing but vigorous rhythm (5)
10 Animal (5)
11 La Giaconda, the --- Lisa (4)
13 Small child (3)

CROSSWORD
a Day!

ACROSS
1 Leafy vegetable (7)
6 Warrior in Greek mythology (4)
8 Nymph who loved Narcissus (4)
11 Sheeplike (5)
12 1970s hairstyle (4)
14 Male deer (4)
15 Film clips used as an advertisement (7)

DOWN
2 Fight with gloves (3)
3 Wonder (3)
4 Distant (7)
5 Study of animals (7)
7 Secret love affair (5)
9 Fissure (5)
10 Not well-lit (3)
13 Egg cells (3)
14 --- Mineo, actor (3)

DAY 125

CROSSWORD a Day!

ACROSS
1 Private soldier (7)
6 Sphere (3)
7 Chinese river (7)
8 Throw (a shadow) (4)
9 Went down (4)
12 Character in *The Wizard of Oz* (7)
14 Signal for action (3)
15 Subatomic particle (7)

DOWN
1 Attempt (3)
2 Squeals like a pig (5)
3 Spongy tissue in an orange (4)
4 Fish eggs (3)
5 (Taken) by surprise (5)
8 Pattern of small squares (5)
10 Change (5)
11 German woman! (4)
12 Lair (3)
13 Craving (3)

CROSSWORD
a Day!

ACROSS
1 Quentin ---,
   cult director (9)
6 Wholeness (5)
7 Italian greeting (4)
9 Son of Abraham (5)
10 Owl sound (4)
12 Pilfer (5)
13 *Brief* ---, film (9)

DOWN
2 Parent's sister (4)
3 Creative person (6)
4 Relating to
   Asian languages (5)
5 Loop in a river (5)
7 Swiss political
   division (6)
8 Portion (5)
9 Order of classical
   architecture (5)
11 Story (4)

CROSSWORD a Day!

ACROSS
1 Capital of Poland (6)
6 Contest (4)
7 In working order (6)
9 Neutral (9)
11 Foolishness (6)
12 Satellite of planet (4)
13 Machine (6)

DOWN
2 Expect (6)
3 Underwater vessel (9)
4 Hulk Hogan's sport (9)
5 Observe (3)
8 French dance (6)
10 Little devil (3)

DAY 128

CROSSWORD a Day!

ACROSS
3 Remains! (5)
6 Masculine (4)
7 Domain (5)
8 Irish province (6)
10 Person in charge of a newspaper (6)
11 Horrible (5)
12 Diagram (4)
13 *Dallas* surname (5)

DOWN
1 Emergency vehicle (9)
2 Dismissive (5)
4 Prophet (4)
5 Smiling in an ingratiating way (9)
7 Willing, resolved (5)
9 Construction for climbing a fence (5)
10 Prince William's old school (4)

CROSSWORD
a Day!

ACROSS
5 Area around the South Pole (9)
7 Notoriety (6)
9 Rainbow hue (6)
12 US country music capital (9)

DOWN
1 Amulet (8)
2 Supporting stick (6)
3 Spruce (4)
4 Pig's enclosure (3)
6 Native American tribe (8)
8 Move furtively (6)
10 Armed service (4)
11 Snake (3)

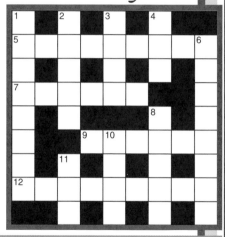

DAY 130

CROSSWORD a Day!

ACROSS
1 Tennis pitch (5)
5 Movie (4)
6 Make the sound of a horse (5)
8 One or the other (6)
10 Marlon ---, actor (6)
12 Nitwit (5)
13 Dark blue (4)
14 Massage (dough) (5)

DOWN
1 Secondary wife (9)
2 Anger (4)
3 Battle (5)
4 Stamped (9)
7 Asian language (5)
9 Split in two (5)
11 Chief of the Norse gods (4)

CROSSWORD
a Day!

ACROSS
3 Operatic song (4)
5 Sallow (6)
6 At a distance (4)
7 Broadsheet, eg (9)
10 Branch (4)
11 Calmed (6)
12 Look after (4)

DOWN
1 Frog's eggs (5)
2 Probable (9)
3 Resolutely (9)
4 Incensed (5)
8 Heather (5)
9 Noisy (5)

CROSSWORD
a Day!

ACROSS
1 Comedian (5)
6 Abode (5)
7 Writing style (5)
8 Terrible (5)
9 Bundle (5)
12 Back street (5)
13 Legitimate (5)
14 Rustic house (5)

DOWN
1 Gag (4)
2 Cognition (9)
3 Greek goddess (4)
4 Completed to perfection (9)
5 Small compartment (4)
9 Food seasoning (4)
10 Let drop (4)
11 Unit of force (4)

DAY 133

CROSSWORD
a Day!

ACROSS
- 4 Away (3)
- 6 Queasiness (6)
- 7 Stimulate into action (9)
- 10 Resolve (9)
- 12 Effect of a long flight (3,3)
- 13 Receive (3)

DOWN
- 1 Wild ass (6)
- 2 People in general (6)
- 3 Surplus (9)
- 5 Bubble (4)
- 8 Frozen droplet (6)
- 9 Appear (6)
- 11 Great lake (4)

LAGOON BOOKS

CROSSWORD
a Day!

ACROSS
1 Amino, eg (4)
4 Stair (4)
7 Country in South America (9)
8 Earring (4)
10 Bill (4)
12 Country in southern Africa (9)
13 Wit, --- Coward (4)
14 On top of (4)

DOWN
2 Comb of feathers (5)
3 Fear, worry (5)
5 That place (5)
6 Practical joke (5)
8 Actress, --- Sarandon (5)
9 Habitual practice (5)
10 Bear in *The Jungle Book* (5)
11 Film, --- *Hall* (5)

CROSSWORD a Day!

ACROSS
1 Changeable (8)
5 Circuit (3)
6 Drink made of apples (5)
7 Afresh (4)
9 Barrier (4)
13 Brush (5)
14 Pole for rowing (3)
15 Retriever dog (8)

DOWN
1 Holiday home (5)
2 Indian currency (5)
3 Curved structure (4)
4 Build (5)
8 Handrail support (5)
10 Audibly (5)
11 Mistake (5)
12 Spiked wheel on a boot (4)

DAY 136

CROSSWORD
a Day!

ACROSS
1 Healthy (3)
3 Stun (4)
5 Boxing film (5)
6 --- Grier, actress (3)
8 Standard quantity (4)
9 Look at intently (4)
11 Ernie ---, golfer (3)
13 Public square (5)
14 Pigment (5)
15 First woman? (3)

DOWN
1 Wealth (7)
2 Strategy (7)
3 --- of Thunder, film (4)
4 Greek letter (3)
6 Parcel (7)
7 Collated fragments of film (7)
10 Skewer (4)
12 Meadow (3)

CROSSWORD
a Day!

ACROSS
1 Film with Juliette Binoche (8)
5 Public house (3)
6 Tarka, eg (5)
7 Plant with fronds (4)
9 Security body (4)
13 Residence (5)
14 Imp (3)
15 Cult film, --- & I (8)

DOWN
1 Tribal head (5)
2 Proprietor (5)
3 Instrument (4)
4 Special present (5)
8 Arm joint (5)
10 Sphere of action (5)
11 Entrails (5)
12 Scott Evil in the Austin Powers films, --- Green (4)

CROSSWORD a Day!

ACROSS
1 Otherwise (4)
3 Small arrow (4)
7 Relating to sound equipment (5)
8 Fastener (3)
9 *Halloween* Director, --- Craven (3)
10 And so on (3)
11 Nevertheless (3)
13 Illness (3)
14 Gaseous layer (5)
15 Entrance corridor (4)
16 Weaponry (4)

DOWN
1 British queen (9)
2 Exchange (4)
4 Confess (4)
5 Book of synonyms (9)
6 Issue (7)
12 Work hard (4)
13 Be frightened of (4)

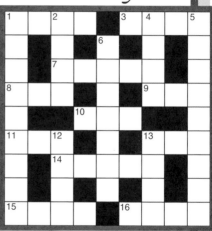

DAY 139

CROSSWORD
a Day!

ACROSS
1. Seaside (5)
6. Solitary (5)
7. From Louisiana (cuisine) (5)
9. Long narrow strap for guiding a horse (4)
10. Outlook (4)
14. Small committee (5)
15. Hidden store of ammunition (5)
16. Click language (5)

DOWN
2. Tooth covering (6)
3. Set of cards dealt (4)
4. Pea case (3)
5. Actress, --- Ryan (3)
8. Alcove (6)
11. Highest point (4)
12. Play a part (3)
13. Video player (1,1,1)

CROSSWORD a Day!

ACROSS
1 Syrian capital (8)
6 Overexcited response (8)
8 Danny ---, comic actor (4)
9 A long way off (4)
12 Literary tool (8)
14 Microscopic organisms (8)

DOWN
2 Dim (5)
3 Broth (4)
4 Kill Bill actress, --- Thurman (3)
5 Hirsute (5)
7 Cut corners (5)
10 Ground grain (5)
11 Place, location (4)
13 Afternoon meal (3)

CROSSWORD a Day!

ACROSS
1 Card game (8)
5 Male cat (3)
6 Planet's path (5)
7 Three feet (4)
9 The --- Piper of Hamelin, tale (4)
13 Let down (5)
14 Quick swim (3)
15 Agricultural area (8)

DOWN
1 Insignificant (5)
2 Stopwatch (5)
3 English school (4)
4 Omit part of (a word) (5)
8 Cold, remote (5)
10 --- rubber tree, plant (5)
11 Tricked (5)
12 Slim (4)

CROSSWORD
a Day!

ACROSS
1 Audio format (1,1)
2 Invited (5)
7 Pounce (5)
8 Away (3)
9 Row of houses (4)
10 Stupor (4)
12 --- Lupino, actress (3)
13 *Roxanne* Singer (5)
14 Actor-director,
   --- Eastwood (5)
15 Spielberg film (1,1)

DOWN
1 Country,
   capital Bogota (8)
3 Casserole (4)
4 Financial (8)
5 Winter missile (8)
6 Direct (8)
11 High-speed
   information
   transfer (1,1,1,1)

CROSSWORD
a Day!

ACROSS
- **2** Field (7)
- **5** Large reptile (9)
- **7** Love (5)
- **12** Large reptile (9)
- **14** Lengthen (7)

DOWN
- **1** Mechanism for slowing down (5)
- **2** Dance (5)
- **3** Delve (3)
- **4** Chicken run (4)
- **6** Freshen (a room) (3)
- **8** Michael J. Fox film, --- *Hollywood* (3)
- **9** Singer, --- Piaf (5)
- **10** Welcome, acknowledge (5)
- **11** Horse speed (4)
- **13** Cereal plant (3)

DAY 144

CROSSWORD

a Day!

ACROSS
1 Royal headwear (5)
3 Wield (3)
6 Go out (sea) (3)
7 Tranquility (5)
9 Ponderous (4)
11 Woman (4)
13 Muscular contraction (5)
14 Green vegetable (3)
15 Your (archaic) (3)
16 Christian leader (5)

DOWN
1 Board game (5)
4 Expressed (5)
5 Instrument (5)
8 Marsh (5)
10 List, roll (5)
12 Irish poet (5)

CROSSWORD
a Day!

ACROSS
1 Holy city (9)
6 Incandescent (5)
7 Saloon (3)
8 Badger's home (4)
10 Clean with water (4)
13 Choose (3)
14 Pop star, --- John (5)
15 Rubbing (9)

DOWN
2 Bird of prey (5)
3 Stitched (4)
4 Constellation of the scales (5)
5 Month (5)
8 Small vessel (5)
9 Complete (5)
11 Piece of cutlery (5)
12 Rudolf ---, last inmate of Spandau Prison (4)

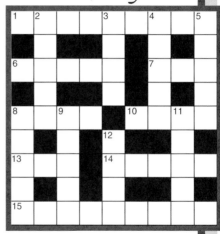

CROSSWORD
a Day!

ACROSS
1 Bucket (4)
3 Candid (4)
6 Sun-dried brick (5)
7 Candle material (3)
8 Servitude (7)
13 Flatfish (3)
14 Shuteye! (5)
15 Chat (4)
16 Stepped (4)

DOWN
1 Summit (4)
2 Country (5)
4 Ability to act (5)
5 Ensuing (4)
9 True, trustworthy (5)
10 Social distinction (5)
11 Delivered legal command (4)
12 Went fast (4)

CROSSWORD
a Day!

ACROSS
1 Antic, jape (5)
4 Weapon (3)
5 Articulate (8)
7 Pip, grain (4)
8 Summon (4)
11 Marriage to more than one woman (8)
13 Automobile (3)
14 Finished (5)

DOWN
1 Dairy product (6)
2 Susceptible (5)
3 Defeat decisively (4)
4 Actor, --- Affleck (3)
6 Performed (6)
9 Formal recognition of achievement (5)
10 Greek harp (4)
12 *One of --- Dinosaurs is Missing*, film (3)

CROSSWORD a Day!

ACROSS
3 *James and the Giant* ---, novel (5)
6 Cowboys' display (5)
7 Actress, --- Witherspoon (5)
8 Very large tree (7)
12 Dog breed (5)
14 Synthetic material (5)
15 Strained (5)

DOWN
1 Lake, --- Sea (4)
2 Muddle, confuse (5)
3 Spiny creature (9)
4 Beer (3)
5 Part of the foot (4)
9 Rustic utopia (5)
10 Hibernian person (4)
11 Someone from Copenhagen (4)
13 Sprint (3)

DAY 149

CROSSWORD
a Day!

ACROSS
1 Type of confectionery (5)
4 Small space (3)
6 Crooner, --- King Cole (3)
8 Road race (5)
12 Monster (4)
13 Speech defect (4)
14 TV detective, --- Mason (5)
17 Definitive period of time (3)
19 J F Kennedy's brother (3)
20 Number of musketeers (5)

DOWN
1 Enthusiast, follower (3)
2 Speck (3)
3 Head of corn (3)
4 Pomade (3)
5 Give money for services (3)
7 Present (a point of view) (5)
9 Associate, accomplice (4)
10 Unsuccessful person (5)
11 Close (4)
14 Peach stone (3)
15 Rocker, --- Stewart (3)
16 Up to now (3)
17 Commit a sin (3)
18 Lincoln's nickname (3)

DAY 150

CROSSWORD a Day!

ACROSS
1 Half open (4)
3 Blackleg (4)
7 Comic character? (9)
8 Number of commandments (3)
10 Possessed (3)
12 Stargazing (9)
13 Roof part (4)
14 Canvas dwelling (4)

DOWN
2 Unit of energy (5)
4 Top of the milk! (5)
5 Bodily fluid (5)
6 Vermillion (7)
8 Cooked sliced bread (5)
9 South African state (5)
11 Jordan's capital (5)

DAY 151

CROSSWORD a Day!

ACROSS
1 Move in water (4)
3 Instrument (4)
7 Jewel (8)
9 Snakelike fish (3)
10 Lacking water (3)
14 Noah's boat (3)
15 Type of terrier (8)
16 Domesticate (4)
17 Nuisance (4)

DOWN
2 Bet (5)
4 Part of a plant (4)
5 Come across (4)
6 With legs apart (7)
8 & 14D Israeli airline (2,2)
11 Newspapers (5)
12 Set of actors (4)
13 Ghastly, sinister (4)
14 See 8D

CROSSWORD
a Day!

ACROSS
1 Franz ---, composer (5)
3 Unfriendly, hostile (3)
6 Mormon state (4)
7 Ground, territory (4)
8 Country (9)
13 Native Peruvian (4)
14 Decline (4)
15 Which person (3)
16 Mad (5)

DOWN
1 --- Dern, actress (5)
2 Colloquialisms (5)
4 Film, --- the Barbarian (5)
5 Scheme (4)
9 Cattle farm (5)
10 Test (4)
11 Donald Trump's ex-wife (5)
12 Outdoor passage (5)

DAY 153

CROSSWORD

a Day!

ACROSS
1 Sufficient (5)
5 Horseback sport (4)
8 Type of cuisine (3-3)
9 Actor, --- Harris (2)
11 Film, --- Girl (2)
12 Scary movie (6)
14 East of ---, novel (4)
15 Large aquatic rodent (5)

DOWN
2 Stand-in (5)
3 Group of kangaroos (3)
4 Denounce (7)
6 Trod heavily (7)
7 Educate (5)
10 Team race (5)
13 Spirit, energy (3)

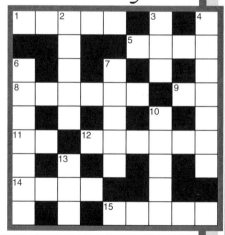

CROSSWORD a Day!

ACROSS
1 Travel document (8)
6 Person who eats other people (8)
8 Profound (4)
9 Thing that a barber cuts (4)
12 Envoy (8)
14 Type of firework (8)

DOWN
2 Humiliation (5)
3 Unit of volume (4)
4 Chest bone (3)
5 Administrative employee (5)
7 Viper (5)
10 Month (5)
11 Exploitative person (4)
13 Mischievous sprite (3)

SOLUTION FOR DAY 153

Across 1. Ample 5. Polo 8. Tex-Mex 9. Ed 11. *My* 12. *Scream* 14. *Eden* 15. Coypu **Down** 2. Proxy 3. Mob 4. Condemn 6. Stomped 7. Teach 10. Relay 13. Pep

CROSSWORD
a Day!

ACROSS

1 Scheme (4)
5 Film, *Play --- For Me* (5)
7 Comfort (7)
8 Abscond (3,4)
11 Where Jesus was crucified (7)
13 *Being ---*, film (5)
14 Necklace part (4)

DOWN

1 Fill (a suitcase) (4)
2 Proclaim (8)
3 Olive, eg (3)
4 Unit of memory (4)
5 Unfixed (7)
6 Divide (8)
9 Strongly dislike (4)
10 Looked at (4)
12 *O Brother, Where --- Thou?*, film (3)

CROSSWORD
a Day!

ACROSS
- **1** Lass (4)
- **3** Scottish lake (4)
- **7** Abode (8)
- **9** US intelligence agency (3)
- **10** Of glands above the kidneys (7)
- **13** Crowd (3)
- **14** Diversified (8)
- **15** Extinct bird (4)
- **16** Sickens (4)

DOWN
- **2** Asian country (5)
- **4** Japanese art of paper-folding (7)
- **5** --- Grant, actor (4)
- **6** Articulacy (7)
- **8** Tottered (7)
- **11** Nearby (5)
- **12** Marsh plant (4)

DAY 157

CROSSWORD a Day!

ACROSS
1 Fantastic (9)
6 & 7D Bangles song (5,6)
7 Have to (4)
9 Characteristic spirit of a community (5)
10 Depend (4)
12 Imbecile (5)
13 Cemetery (9)

DOWN
2 Country whose capital is Muscat (4)
3 Delicate (6)
4 Central point (5)
5 High (5)
7 See 6A
8 Minor crash (5)
9 --- Doolittle, My Fair Lady character (5)
11 Laugh loudly (4)

CROSSWORD
a Day!

ACROSS
1 Insist upon (6)
6 Effortless (4)
7 Haphazard (6)
9 Companion of Robin Hood (5,4)
11 Peninsula in Europe (6)
12 Unfastened (4)
13 Seal (6)

DOWN
2 Sparkling (6)
3 Captivating (9)
4 Femme fatale (9)
5 Shade (3)
8 Writer (6)
10 Sorrow (3)

SOLUTION FOR DAY 157

Across 1. Wonderful 6. *Manic* 7. Ethos 10. Rely 12. Idiot 13. Graveyard
Down 2. Oman 3. Dainty 4. *Focus* 5. Lofty 7. *Monday* 8. Prang 9. Eliza 11. Roar

DAY 159

CROSSWORD a Day!

ACROSS

- **3** Loathe (5)
- **6** Promise (4)
- **7** Imprisons (5)
- **8** Play, *The --- Cometh* (6)
- **10** Resolve (6)
- **11** Claude ---, painter (5)
- **12** German man's title (4)
- **13** Mary Poppins' job title (5)

DOWN

- **1** Law enforcer (9)
- **2** Scatter (5)
- **4** See 10D
- **5** Dark red fruit (9)
- **7** Military trainee (5)
- **9** Tearjerker, *--- Magnolias* (5)
- **10 & 4D** Boromir in *The Lord of the Rings* (4,4)

SOLUTION FOR DAY 158

Across 1. Assert 6. Easy 7. Random 9. Friar Tuck 11. Iberia 12. Open 13. Gasket **Down** 2. Starry 3. Endearing 4. Temptress 5. Dye 8. Scribe 10. Woe

DAY 160

CROSSWORD

a Day!

ACROSS
5 Disreputable (9)
7 'I've found it' (6)
9 Be curious about (6)
12 Thief (9)

DOWN
1 Worldwide crime force (8)
2 Hoard (5)
3 Journey (4)
4 Word of disapproval (3)
6 Drench (8)
8 Confess (6)
10 Portent (4)
11 Cook in oil (3)

DAY 161

CROSSWORD
a Day!

ACROSS
1. Dense (5)
5. Inflatable (4)
6. Film, *The Full ---* (5)
8. Number (6)
10. Place of worship (6)
12. Early version of a document (5)
13. Loch containing a monster? (4)
14. Bury (5)

DOWN
1. Grave marker (9)
2. Sweet, adorable (4)
3. Bill ---, *Love Actually* actor (5)
4. Artificial material (9)
7. Give up (5)
9. Mennonite sect (5)
11. Film, *--- Brockovich* (4)

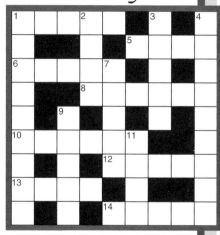

DAY 162

CROSSWORD
a Day!

ACROSS
3 Large US cat (4)
5 Referee (6)
6 Ark-builder (4)
7 Idiosyncratic (9)
10 Indonesian island (4)
11 Tempt (6)
12 Part of a plant (4)

DOWN
1 Leap (5)
2 Incredulity (9)
3 Pierce (9)
4 City in Florida (5)
8 Rub (5)
9 Humped animal (5)

CROSSWORD
a Day!

ACROSS
1 Type of parrot (5)
6 Shrubby herb (5)
7 Deliberate (5)
8 Precise (5)
9 Transfer paper (5)
12 Egg-shaped (5)
13 Puccini opera (5)
14 Relative (5)

DOWN
1 Traditional story (4)
2 Expression of disapproval (9)
3 Ended sleep (4)
4 Voice amplifier (9)
5 Animal fur (4)
9 Show affection (4)
10 Hire out (4)
11 Wood-shaping tool (4)

DAY 164

CROSSWORD a Day!

ACROSS
4 --- Johnson, aviator (3)
6 Brewing vessel (6)
7 Corresponding (9)
10 Amount granted (9)
12 Joyous shout (6)
13 Grain (3)

DOWN
1 Canada's capital (6)
2 Package (6)
3 Woebegone (9)
5 Arithmetic average (4)
8 Snub (6)
9 German poet (6)
11 --- Tomlin, actress (4)

CROSSWORD
a Day!

ACROSS
1 Small branch (4)
4 Kevin Spacey film (1-3)
7 *Cheers* actor (3,6)
8 Comedy sketch (4)
10 Went (4)
12 Fizzy (9)
13 Level (4)
14 Film, --- *Wide Shut* (4)

DOWN
2 Destroy (5)
3 Samuel Beckett play *Waiting for ---* (5)
5 Light adhesive (5)
6 Element (5)
8 *Wake Up Little ---*, song (5)
9 Trifling (5)
10 Lump (5)
11 *Sesame Street* Bert's friend (5)

CROSSWORD
a Day!

ACROSS
1 Tiny payment (8)
5 Scarper (3)
6 Two under par (5)
7 Grandee (4)
9 Blast of air (4)
13 Sagacity (5)
14 Garland (3)
15 Appetizer (8)

DOWN
1 Jeopardy (5)
2 Singing voice (5)
3 Feeling of wonderment (4)
4 Island in New York bay (5)
8 Last of a series (5)
10 Dark (5)
11 Embezzler (5)
12 Deride (4)

DAY 167

CROSSWORD
a Day!

ACROSS
1 Rubbish, junk (3)
3 Poke (4)
5 Data (5)
6 Baby's bed (3)
8 Utensil (4)
9 Mark (4)
11 Harry Potter's chum, --- Weasley (3)
13 Pleasant smell (5)
14 Following (5)
15 High self-opinion (3)

DOWN
1 Hurricane film (7)
2 Tropical storm (7)
3 Trail (4)
4 *Scooby* ---, film (3)
6 Whirlwind (7)
7 Violent tempest (7)
10 Den (4)
12 Rotten (3)

DAY 168

CROSSWORD
a Day!

ACROSS
1. Rim (4)
3. Mamma ---, singer (4)
7. Pacific island (5)
8. Mimic (3)
9. Sea (9)
12. Awkward fool (3)
13. Actor, --- Hawke (5)
14. Simplicity (4)
15. Skin of a fruit (4)

DOWN
2. Princess, mother of William and Harry (5)
4. Conscious (5)
5. Rear of a ship (5)
6. Fizz (7)
9. Domestic task (5)
10. --- Sewell, actor (5)
11. Stun (5)

DAY 169

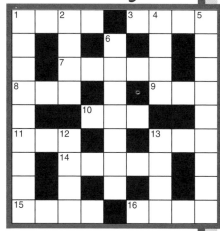

CROSSWORD a Day!

ACROSS
1 Recreational area (4)
3 Period (4)
7 Tooth (5)
8 Heart of a storm (3)
9 See 10A
10 & 9A *The Hulk* director (3,3)
11 Porcine animal (3)
13 Railing (3)
14 *Me, Myself and ---*, Jim Carrey film (5)
15 First garden? (4)
16 Eyelid swelling (4)

DOWN
1 Tropical fruit (9)
2 Italian capital (4)
4 Aristocrat (4)
5 Falling star (9)
6 Defamation (7)
12 Donate (4)
13 Gain victory over (4)

CROSSWORD
a Day!

ACROSS
1 Talk (5)
6 See 15A
7 Glower (5)
9 Linseed plant (4)
10 From Istanbul? (4)
14 Complain feebly (5)
15 & 6A *American Idol* judge (5,5)
16 Drinker (5)

DOWN
2 *The Color* ---, film (6)
3 Immanuel ---, philosopher (4)
4 Poem (3)
5 Muhammad ---, boxing champion (3)
8 Fruit (6)
11 Kill (a fly) (4)
12 Health resort (3)
13 Public transport (3)

DAY 171

CROSSWORD
a Day!

ACROSS
1 Running competition (4)
5 Actor, --- McQueen (5)
7 Low wall on a roof (7)
8 Bandaged (7)
11 Casual shoes (7)
13 Islamic meat (5)
14 Plant, --- vera (4)

DOWN
1 Ready to eat (4)
2 English county (8)
3 Consumed (3)
4 Nought (4)
5 Depth perception, --- awareness (7)
6 Celestial (8)
9 Painful (4)
10 Island (4)
12 Rowing equipment (3)

SOLUTION FOR DAY 170

Across 1. Speak 6. Abdul 7. Frown 9. Flax 10. Turk 14. Whine 15. Paula 16. Toper Down 2. *Purple* 3. Kant 4. Ode 5. Ali 8. Orange 11. Swat 12. Spa 13. Bus

CROSSWORD a Day!

ACROSS
1 Visibly upset (7)
6 Creeping plant (3)
7 At no location (7)
8 Military vehicle (4)
9 Turned round (4)
12 Soft flat cake eaten toasted (7)
14 Pigeon's sound (3)
15 Children's author, --- Potter (7)

DOWN
1 Heavy weight (3)
2 *The Lord of the Rings'* Elven princess (5)
3 Bedrock resident, --- Flintstone (4)
4 Falsehood (3)
5 Romantic poet (5)
8 Railway (5)
10 Kilted musician? (5)
11 Large fish (4)
12 Male swan (3)
13 Stretch, challenge (3)

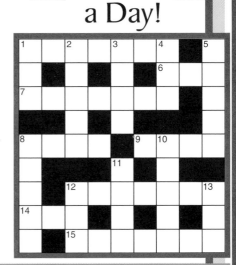

DAY 173

CROSSWORD a Day!

ACROSS

1 For this reason (2)
2 Nonsense (5)
7 Reagan's wife (5)
8 --- Marvin, actor (3)
9 Feeble (4)
10 Locks (4)
12 Pool stick (3)
13 Biblical name (5)
14 David ---, singer (5)
15 --- *will rock you*, song (2)

DOWN

1 Bread snack (8)
3 *Wide Sargasso Sea* author, Jean --- (4)
4 Tangible (8)
5 Training shoes (8)
6 Dreadful (8)
11 4,840 square yards (4)

CROSSWORD
a Day!

ACROSS
2 Anteater (7)
5 Highest range of peaks (9)
7 Long lock of hair (5)
12 Large hills (9)
14 Party-pooper (7)

DOWN
1 See 13D
2 M. --- Walsh, actor (5)
3 Computer in *2001: A Space Odyssey* (3)
4 --- Wyle, *ER* actor (4)
6 Equine animal (3)
8 Manage (3)
9 Prickly (5)
10 Delicious (5)
11 --- Bear, cartoon character (4)
13 & 1D Mausoleum at Agra (3,5)

CROSSWORD a Day!

ACROSS
1 Iberian country (5)
3 See 11A
6 Encourage, --- on (3)
7 See 11A
9 Typeface (4)
11 & 14A & 3A & 7A Disney film (4,3,3,5)
13 Barely sufficient (5)
14 See 11A
15 Young fish (3)
16 Heavenly creature (5)

DOWN
1 Ledge (5)
4 Warm and damp (5)
5 Verily (5)
8 Proverb: A rolling --- gathers no moss (5)
10 Take place (5)
12 Sing Swiss-style (5)

CROSSWORD
a Day!

ACROSS
1 Area around 15A (9)
6 Buffalo (5)
7 Girl's name (3)
8 Money owed (4)
10 Celebrity (4)
13 Actor, --- Diesel (3)
14 Store of valuables (5)
15 Amundsen's conquest (5,4)

DOWN
2 Artless, innocent (5)
3 Smallest animal (4)
4 Place one's faith in (5)
5 Preside (5)
8 Judy ---, actress (5)
9 African languages (5)
11 Block in a forge (5)
12 *The Seven Year ---*, film (4)

CROSSWORD
a Day!

ACROSS
1 & 3A Star of 5D (4,4)
3 See 1A
6 See 8A
7 Artificial language (3)
8 & 6A Star of 5D (7,5)
13 Assistance (3)
14 Strike, hit (5)
15 & 16A Star of 5D (4,4)
16 See 15A

DOWN
1 Film about a pig (4)
2 Quaintly amusing (5)
4 *The* ---, epic poem (5)
5 Film adapted from 4D (4)
9 Lines inside a circle (5)
10 Desert (5)
11 Birthday food (4)
12 TV series, ---, *Warrior Princess* (4)

DAY 178

CROSSWORD
a Day!

ACROSS
1 Sly Stallone film (5)
4 Large tank (3)
5 Festival (8)
7 Above (4)
8 King who built a dyke (4)
11 *The Lion, the Witch and the ---*, book (8)
13 Hoover, eg (3)
14 Homeless, lost (5)

DOWN
1 Suppose (6)
2 Osmond sister (5)
3 US state (4)
4 By way of (3)
6 Place where cakes are made (6)
9 Bread ingredient (5)
10 Probability (4)
12 Branch (3)

CROSSWORD
a Day!

ACROSS
3 Small wood (5)
6 Bash, do (5)
7 Texan farm (5)
8 Mythical creature (7)
12 Wireless (5)
14 Pasta quills (5)
15 Emblem worn as a mark of office (5)

DOWN
1 Luncheon meat (4)
2 Hobbit, --- Baggins (5)
3 Navigation tool (9)
4 Particular (3)
5 Reverberation (4)
9 --- Monsoon, *Absolutely Fabulous* character (5)
10 Crustacean (4)
11 Move (a muscle) (4)
13 Father (3)

DAY 180

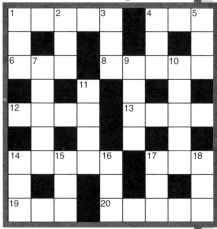

CROSSWORD a Day!

ACROSS
1. Regal (5)
4. Sorrowful (3)
6. End (of a finger) (3)
8. Wesley Snipes film (5)
12. Remaining, otherwise (4)
13. Revolving indicator of wind direction (4)
14. Fossilized tree sap (5)
17. Chart music (3)
19. Social insect (3)
20. Actress, --- Grable (5)

DOWN
1. Sewer rodent (3)
2. High-pitched bark (3)
3. Tennis shot (3)
4. Curative mineral spring (3)
5. Pass away (3)
7. Middle Eastern religion (5)
9. Tennis score (4)
10. Australian wild dog (5)
11. Actor, --- Hackman (4)
14. Range (3)
15. However (3)
16. Chest bone (3)
17. Domesticated animal (3)
18. Snoop (3)

CROSSWORD a Day!

ACROSS
1 Tiff (4)
3 See 8D
7 State of being (9)
8 Crimson (3)
10 Newt (3)
12 Political theory (9)
13 Scottish island (4)
14 Ghetto drama,
   --- *N The Hood* (4)

DOWN
2 Creature like
   a fairy (5)
4 --- Oakley,
   markswoman (5)
5 Vote into office (5)
6 Breastplate (7)
8 & 3A Chat show
   host (5,4)
9 Evil spirit (5)
11 Suspicious (5)

DAY 182

CROSSWORD a Day!

ACROSS

1 Body's surface (4)
3 Swindle (4)
7 Kennel (8)
9 Early pseudonym for Charles Dickens (3)
10 Ewer (3)
14 Rock band, --- Jovi (3)
15 Mechanism used to regulate machinery (8)
16 Stink (4)
17 Poet, --- Angelou (4)

DOWN

2 Glory (5)
4 Seizure of power (4)
5 Contact (4)
6 Mental function (7)
8 Wizard's home! (2)
11 Pirates' flag, --- Roger (5)
12 A long way away (4)
13 Eight bits (4)
14 *Let It ---,* Beatles classic (2)

CROSSWORD
a Day!

ACROSS
1 Settling of a bill (7)
6 Mineral rock (3)
7 Take the chair (7)
8 Sea movement (4)
9 Seagull (4)
12 Comedy series about six pals (7)
14 Actor, --- Majors (3)
15 Kurt Cobain's band (7)

DOWN
1 Explode (3)
2 Produce (5)
3 Give out (4)
4 Digit (3)
5 Muslim holy city (5)
8 Reckoning (5)
10 African country (5)
11 Fibber (4)
12 Low marshy area (3)
13 Ocean (3)

CROSSWORD
a Day!

ACROSS
1 Heavy rain (8)
6 & 11D Adam and Eve's first home (6,2,4)
8 Ship's hands (4)
9 Footwear (4)
12 Heaven (8)
14 Ray of lunar light (8)

DOWN
2 Marine animal (5)
3 Blocks which press on the brake discs (4)
4 Ancient vase (3)
5 Frequently (5)
7 Range (5)
10 Hurry (5)
11 See 6A
13 --- di Janeiro, Brazilian city (3)

LAGOON BOOKS

DAY 185

CROSSWORD
a Day!

ACROSS
1 European country, capital Vienna (7)
6 Island where Napoleon was first exiled (4)
8 Wild pig (4)
11 Tennis player, --- Ivanisevic (5)
12 Hideous (4)
14 Shop selling prepared foods (4)
15 European country, capital Copenhagen (7)

DOWN
2 Style of music (3)
3 Steal from (3)
4 European country, capital Brussels (7)
5 European country, capital Zagreb (7)
7 Hard ring-shaped roll (5)
9 Unit of measurement (5)
10 Married woman's title (3)
13 Japanese currency (3)
14 Genetic material (1,1,1)

CROSSWORD
a Day!

ACROSS
1 Hunted animal (4)
3 Slip on wheels (4)
7 Pink bird (8)
9 Character from *The Matrix* (3)
10 Happiness (3)
14 Kind (3)
15 Abstemiousness (8)
16 Reduced prices (4)
17 Dispatch (4)

DOWN
2 Have recourse (5)
4 Hereditary ruler (4)
5 Let go of (4)
6 Pungent gas (7)
8 Look! (2)
11 Errol ---, actor (5)
12 Egyptian goddess (4)
13 Cain's brother (4)
14 That thing (2)

CROSSWORD
a Day!

ACROSS
1 Jack ---, actor (9)
6 Sly verbal attack (5)
7 Cut (4)
9 The face that launched a thousand ships (5)
10 Ursine animal (4)
12 Peter ---, actor (5)
13 1960s seminal road movie (4,5)

DOWN
2 Pubs (4)
3 Dennis ---, actor (6)
4 Killed (5)
5 Crannies (5)
7 Essential oil (6)
8 Tolerate, endure (5)
9 Underworld (5)
11 Move gradually (towards) (4)

CROSSWORD
a Day!

ACROSS
1 Scamp (6)
6 Distinctive air (4)
7 Jacuzzi (3,3)
9 Practice run (9)
11 Annoy (6)
12 Verdi opera (4)
13 City of Pakistan (6)

DOWN
2 Professed (6)
3 Large church (9)
4 Maze (9)
5 Uncooked (3)
8 Mariner (6)
10 Slack (3)

CROSSWORD
a Day!

ACROSS

3 *Inferno* writer (5)
6 Covered with burnt embers (4)
7 & 8A Country and Western singer (5,6)
8 See 7A
10 Paris landmark, --- Tower (6)
11 Slight admixture (of a feeling) (5)
12 Metal disc struck to give a loud resonant sound (4)
13 Bread ingredient (5)

DOWN

1 Woodwork (9)
2 Bird sound (5)
4 Unknown author (4)
5 Origin of words (9)
7 *101 Dalmatians* author, --- Smith (5)
9 Progressing (5)
10 Items that should not all be in one basket (4)

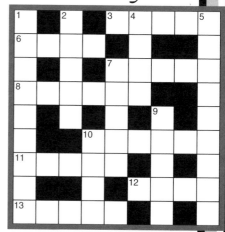

CROSSWORD
a Day!

ACROSS
5 Deserted (9)
7 Creature (6)
9 Reiterate (6)
12 Specialized (9)

DOWN
1 Slingshot (8)
2 Sorcery (5)
3 Notion (4)
4 Writing fluid (3)
6 Delicately (8)
8 Instruct (6)
10 Sicilian volcano (4)
11 Winning serve (3)

CROSSWORD
a Day!

ACROSS
1 Proclamation (5)
5 Karl ---, political thinker (4)
6 Give out (5)
8 King of the Huns (6)
10 European peninsula (6)
12 Coat of arms (5)
13 Style (4)
14 Summer meal (5)

DOWN
1 Full of pep (9)
2 Concluding part (4)
3 Animal (5)
4 Lacking pep (9)
7 Moral rule (5)
9 Fathered (5)
11 Region (4)

SOLUTION FOR DAY 190
Across 5. Abandoned 7. Animal 9. Repeat 12. Technical
Down 1. Catapult 2. Magic 3. Idea 4. Ink 6. Daintily 8. Teach 10. Etna 11. Ace

CROSSWORD
a Day!

ACROSS
1 Shoeless (8)
5 Take in food (3)
6 Happen again (5)
7 Gate (4)
9 Subtract (4)
13 Excepted (5)
14 Diseased (3)
15 Better (8)

DOWN
1 Foodstuff (5)
2 Number relation (5)
3 Blaze (4)
4 Transport vehicle (5)
8 Desert waterhole (5)
10 Legal excuse (5)
11 18th century mathematician (5)
12 At this place (4)

CROSSWORD
a Day!

ACROSS
1 Manly (5)
6 Narrow gorge (5)
7 --- Moore, actor (5)
8 The 'King' of rock and roll (5)
9 Ancient language (5)
12 Discharge (5)
13 Fiddle (5)
14 Rendezvous (5)

DOWN
1 Additional (4)
2 Knowledge (9)
3 Monster (4)
4 Vintage TV comedy series (1,4,4)
5 The one here (4)
9 Passion (4)
10 Tidy (4)
11 Funny story

DAY 194

CROSSWORD
a Day!

ACROSS
4 Attempt (3)
6 Greater (6)
7 Fatigued (9)
10 Tactical (9)
12 Develop (6)
13 Genetic make-up (3)

DOWN
1 Tool (6)
2 Mainstay (6)
3 Alluring (9)
5 Garment (4)
8 Type of switch (6)
9 Act (6)
11 Water down (4)

CROSSWORD
a Day!

ACROSS
1 Treadle (5)
6 Escape (5)
7 Animal (5)
8 Loud (5)
9 Canoe (5)
12 Small island (5)
13 Create artwork (5)
14 Our planet (5)

DOWN
1 Part of the hand (4)
2 Envy or lust, eg (6,3)
3 Healthy, muscular (4)
4 Mountain railway (9)
5 Repudiate (4)
9 Retained (4)
10 Type of hawk (4)
11 Tickle (4)

CROSSWORD
a Day!

ACROSS
1 Buddy (4)
3 Capable (4)
7 Ground (5)
8 Run gently (3)
9 Pyrosis (9)
12 & 6D Presence in Orwell's 1984 (3,7)
13 Draw forth (5)
14 Designer, --- Saint Laurent (4)
15 Superlative (4)

DOWN
2 Split in two (5)
4 Compact (home) (5)
5 Person who took the Marbles to Britain (5)
6 See 12A
9 Pastime (5)
10 Disagree (5)
11 Scrapes up (5)

CROSSWORD
a Day!

ACROSS
1 Sty animal (3)
3 Stopper for a cask (4)
5 Romantic flowers? (5)
6 Illness (3)
8 God of love (4)
9 See 2D
11 Small amount (3)
13 Manly (5)
14 Silly smile (5)
15 *Here Comes the ---,*
   Beatles song (3)

DOWN
1 Film, *The --- Storm* (7)
2 & 9A End-of-era
   drama (7,4)
3 Foundation (4)
4 Hair product (3)
6 Saint of Assisi (7)
7 Mysterious (7)
10 Run ---, rampage (4)
12 Goal (3)

CROSSWORD a Day!

ACROSS
1 Expectorate (4)
3 Thereby, --- facto (4)
7 US 'Watergate' President (5)
8 Make free (3)
9 Type of rule (9)
12 Debt (1,1,1)
13 Custom (5)
14 Actress, --- Beckinsale (4)
15 European mountain range (4)

DOWN
2 Most important (5)
4 Winter coat (5)
5 Strangely (5)
6 Italian dumplings (7)
9 Beverage (5)
10 Climb up (5)
11 Put waves in hair (5)

LAGOON BOOKS

DAY 199

CROSSWORD a Day!

ACROSS

1 Landing for ships (4)
3 Round flat surface (4)
7 Of maritime military (5)
8 Spot (3)
9 Type of tree (3)
10 Stephen ---, actor (3)
11 Unhealthy (3)
13 Vegetable (3)
14 Ire (5)
15 Nephew of
   Donald Duck (4)
16 Border (4)

DOWN

1 Harry Potter's sport (9)
2 Stage musical,
   --- *Misbehavin'* (4)
4 Bone ---, very lazy (4)
5 Sparkling wine (9)
6 Mean, median
   or mode (7)
12 Fine decorative fabric (4)
13 Goad to action (4)

CROSSWORD
a Day!

ACROSS
1 Frighten (5)
6 Perceivable track (5)
7 & 8D Judge on 10A (5,6)
9 Deceased (4)
10 *American ---*, show for wannabes (4)
14 Speleologist (5)
15 Abyss (5)
16 Expulsion (5)

DOWN
2 Shaping tool (6)
3 Sicilian volcano (4)
4 Crone (3)
5 Everyone (3)
8 See 7A
11 Highpoint (4)
12 Playing card (3)
13 Protective piece of carpet (3)

LAGOON BOOKS

CROSSWORD
a Day!

ACROSS

1 Get through a difficult situation (4)
5 Smooth (5)
7 Sir Peter ---, actor (7)
8 Plover (7)
11 Reactive substance (7)
13 West African country (5)
14 Requests (4)

DOWN

1 Constellation of the Southern Cross (4)
2 South Pacific island (8)
3 Twosome (3)
4 *Finding* ---, film (4)
5 Winter statue (7)
6 *The* ---, 1960s TV series (8)
9 Large beer mug with a face, --- jug (4)
10 --- Redding, singer (4)
12 Muslim festival (3)

CROSSWORD a Day!

ACROSS

1 Precisely (7)
6 Long period of time (3)
7 Sea creature (7)
8 Discretion (4)
9 Circuitous trip (4)
12 Agriculture (7)
14 Rebel leader, --- Guevara (3)
15 Saturday and Sunday (7)

DOWN

1 Umberto ---, writer (3)
2 Native Mexican (5)
3 Use keyboard (4)
4 Affirmative! (3)
5 Derisive smile (5)
8 Vestige (5)
10 Popeye's girlfriend, --- Oyl (5)
11 Great Lake (4)
12 Not many (3)
13 Deity (3)

SOLUTION FOR DAY 201

Across 1. Cope 5. Pitcairn 7. Suave 8. Ustinov 11. Reagent 13. Benin 14. Asks Lapwing

Down 1. Crux 2. Pitcairn 3. Duo 4. Nemo 5. Snowman 6. Avengers 9. Toby 10. Otis 12. Eid

CROSSWORD a Day!

ACROSS

1 Bovine animal (2)
2 *When --- Met Sally*, classic comedy (5)
7 Covered entrance (5)
8 Take the weight off one's feet (3)
9 Beach material (4)
10 Air particles (4)
12 & 5D & 13A Cary Elwes film (3,8,5)
13 See 12A
14 Lion in the Chronicles of Narnia (5)
15 Afterthought in a letter (1,1)

DOWN

1 Antonym (8)
3 Dull pain (4)
4 Russian monk (8)
5 See 12A
6 Stammers (8)
11 Swedish pop group (4)

CROSSWORD a Day!

ACROSS
2 Absurd pretence (7)
5 Biblical figure (4,5)
7 Tall, gangly (5)
12 See 3D
14 Volcanic (rock) (7)

DOWN
1 Extra card in the pack (5)
2 Artificial waterway (5)
3 & 12A Shakespearean play, *Antony* --- (3,9)
4 Low platform at the end of a hall (4)
6 *Raiders of the Lost* ---, film (3)
8 In the past (3)
9 Paula ---, Michael Hutchence's lover (5)
10 Journal (5)
11 Promote (4)
13 Continued on the next page (1,1,1)

SOLUTION FOR DAY 203

Across 1. Ox 2. Harry 7. Porch 8. Sit 9. Sand 10. Dust 12. *The* 13. *Bride* 14. Aslan 15. PS **Down** 1. Opposite 3. Ache 4. Rasputin 5. *Princess* 6. Stutters 11. Abba

CROSSWORD
a Day!

ACROSS
1 Stylish talent (5)
3 Baby newt (3)
6 Nocturnal bird (3)
7 Series of links (5)
9 Cash register (4)
11 Turn over and over (4)
13 Wheel part (5)
14 Ornamental carp (3)
15 School sports hall (3)
16 Move rhythmically (5)

DOWN
1 Frozen dew (5)
4 Pleated piece of material (5)
5 Garment (5)
8 Lucky result (5)
10 Implicitly suggest (5)
12 French river (5)

DAY 206

CROSSWORD
a Day!

ACROSS
1 Scene of a 1969 music festival (9)
6 Outrider (5)
7 Road surface (3)
8 Donkey's sound (4)
10 Protein-rich bean (4)
13 & 14A Country (3,5)
14 See 13A
15 Former British Prime Minister (9)

DOWN
2 Wit, --- Wilde (5)
3 Quench (4)
4 Surpass (5)
5 Fate (5)
8 Film, --- *Instinct* (5)
9 Goodbye (5)
11 Country bumpkin (5)
12 Sir --- Guiness, actor (4)

CROSSWORD
a Day!

ACROSS
- 1 Hurl (5)
- 6 Happen (5)
- 7 Subsidiary proposition (5)
- 8 Submerge (5)
- 9 Great meal (5)
- 12 Relative (2-3)
- 13 Evade (5)
- 14 Out of practice (5)

DOWN
- 1 Lofty (4)
- 2 Dutch painter (9)
- 3 Blue dyestuff (4)
- 4 Greek citadel (9)
- 5 Seeds of cereal grains (4)
- 9 Evanesce (4)
- 10 Level (4)
- 11 Swing (4)

CROSSWORD
a Day!

ACROSS
3 Marie ---, scientist (5)
6 Snag (5)
7 Christopher ---, *Superman* actor (5)
8 Artificial substance with many forms (7)
12 Book for stamps (5)
14 Severe (5)
15 Less (5)

DOWN
1 Skin of impurities at the top of a liquid (4)
2 Ring-shaped coral reef around a lagoon (5)
3 Yuletide (9)
4 *Murders in the --- Morgue*, novel (3)
5 Always (4)
9 Inspire, permeate (5)
10 Inside of the hand (4)
11 All-terrain vehicle (4)
13 Container for trash (3)

CROSSWORD
a Day!

ACROSS

1 Fair-haired woman (5)
4 Feline animal (3)
6 --- Air, area of LA (3)
8 Jacket part (5)
12 Amaze (4)
13 Gaming cubes (4)
14 Cause to swell (5)
17 Cunning like a fox (3)
19 Chinese pan (3)
20 Additional payment (5)

DOWN

1 --- Dylan, singer (3)
2 Film star, --- Gibson (3)
3 Cooking liquid (3)
4 Policeman (3)
5 Israeli city, --- Aviv (3)
7 Praise (5)
9 Helper (4)
10 Do very well (5)
11 --- Kournikova, tennis player (4)
14 Front of a ship (3)
15 Type of tree (3)
16 Label (3)
17 Transgression (3)
18 Positive answer (3)

CROSSWORD
a Day!

ACROSS
- 1 & 3A All-terrain vehicle (4,4)
- 3 See 1A
- 7 Lack of fame (9)
- 8 Underwear (3)
- 10 Beach building (3)
- 12 Element (9)
- 13 & 14A Adhesive roll (4,4)
- 14 See 13A

DOWN
- 2 Dark brown (5)
- 4 From Dublin? (5)
- 5 Land of the Pyramids (5)
- 6 Duke's wife? (7)
- 8 Two-legged creature (5)
- 9 *Flowers in the ---*, novel (5)
- 11 Seize power (5)

DAY 211

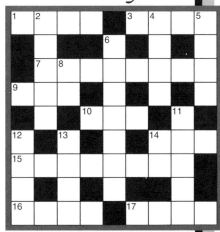

CROSSWORD a Day!

ACROSS
1 Applaud (4)
3 Small fault (4)
7 Lush (8)
9 Charge (3)
10 For what reason (3)
14 Body part (3)
15 Flowering plant (8)
16 Lower (4)
17 Large ring (4)

DOWN
2 Heavily loaded (5)
4 Actor, --- Neeson (4)
5 Broad (4)
6 Actor, --- Hopkins (7)
8 With regard to (2)
11 Guest appearance by a celebrity (5)
12 Elderly (4)
13 Forehead (4)
14 Community of countries (1,1)

SOLUTION FOR DAY 210
Across 1. Quad 3. Bike 7. Obscurity 8. Bra 10. Hut 12. Potassium 13. Duct 14. Tape
Down 2. Umber 4. Irish 5. Egypt 6. Duchess 8. Biped 9. Attic 11. Usurp

LAGOON BOOKS

DAY 212

CROSSWORD a Day!

ACROSS
1 Ascend (5)
5 Festive occasion (4)
6 Interference (5)
8 Comic book reporter (6)
10 Response (6)
12 Restore (5)
13 Fencing sword (4)
14 Weapon (5)

DOWN
1 Material for smoothing wood (9)
2 Mislaid (4)
3 Father Christmas, --- Claus (5)
4 Machine for cutting the grass (9)
7 Swiss mountain (5)
9 Deathly pale (5)
11 Harvest (4)

DAY 213

LAGOON BOOKS

CROSSWORD
a Day!

ACROSS
1 Put off (5)
5 Art movement (4)
8 Element (6)
9 Classic film, --- *the Waterfront* (2)
11 Harmful light (1,1)
12 Film awards show (6)
14 Burn (4)
15 Thrush-like bird (5)

DOWN
2 Ethnic group (5)
3 Wadding (3)
4 Lose lustre (7)
6 Crumple, --- up (7)
7 Shut (5)
10 Fortune-telling cards (5)
13 Naughty (3)

CROSSWORD
a Day!

ACROSS

1 Exact (7)
6 *Chasing* ---, film (3)
7 Ideal (7)
8 Clarified butter (4)
9 Curve (4)
12 Mathematical rule (7)
14 H. Ryder Haggard novel (3)
15 Everlasting (7)

DOWN

1 Dickens' character (3)
2 Eagle's nest (5)
3 Notion (4)
4 Have a meal (3)
5 Talking bird (5)
10 French city (5)
11 Without constraint (4)
12 Charge (3)
13 Everybody (3)

LAGOON BOOKS

DAY 215

CROSSWORD
a Day!

ACROSS
1 Good cause (7)
6 Cut roughly (4)
8 Bond film, *For --- Eyes Only* (4)
11 *Twelfth Night* heroine (5)
12 Word said after experiencing pain (4)
14 Measure of speed (4)
15 *Grease 2* Actor, --- Caulfield (7)

DOWN
2 Great ---, extinct bird (3)
3 *The Holly and the ---*, Christmas carol (3)
4 Hair product (7)
5 Cargo (7)
7 Municipal (5)
9 City in Nebraska (5)
10 --- Voight, actor (3)
13 Bewitch (3)
14 Actress, --- West (3)

CROSSWORD a Day!

ACROSS
1 Wound covering (4)
3 Recedes (4)
7 Tree (8)
9 Japanese Buddhism (3)
10 Diplomatic (7)
13 Plunge (3)
14 Renaissance song (8)
15 Impolite (4)
16 Purply-brown (4)

DOWN
2 Meteor (5)
4 Country (7)
5 Type of bean (4)
6 Decline from (7)
8 Unabetted (7)
11 Flower (5)
12 --- Sharif, actor (4)

CROSSWORD
a Day!

ACROSS
1 Maze (9)
6 Body of troops (5)
7 Location (4)
9 Female dog (5)
10 At no cost (4)
12 Shred (5)
13 Calls to mind (9)

DOWN
2 Nautical call used in hailing (4)
3 1980s stereotype (6)
4 Semi-divine spirit (5)
5 Actor, --- Ledger (5)
7 Sacred beetle (6)
8 Bid (5)
9 Broom (5)
11 Cause trouble by gossiping (4)

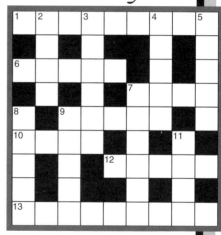

CROSSWORD
a Day!

ACROSS
1 Divide into two (6)
6 Seep (4)
7 Skiing event (6)
9 Mysterious (9)
11 Attempting (6)
12 Cook in oven (4)
13 Conventional (6)

DOWN
2 Away from sea (6)
3 Educate (9)
4 Mark Twain character (3,6)
5 Allow (3)
8 Capital of Austria (6)
10 Japanese sash (3)

DAY 219

CROSSWORD a Day!

ACROSS
3 Cartoon strip magazine (5)
6 --- Murdoch, novelist (4)
7 Complain (5)
8 Exclusive group (6)
10 *The Musicians of* ---, folktale (6)
11 Bitterly pungent (5)
12 Cry of regret (4)
13 Scandinavian 4D (5)

DOWN
1 Villain (9)
2 Period on alert (5)
4 Monster (4)
5 Chinese language (9)
7 Protect (5)
9 Wander along (5)
10 Buffalo ---, William Cody (4)

CROSSWORD
a Day!

ACROSS

5 South American country (9)
7 Line on a weather map (6)
9 Asian temple (6)
12 Way of living (9)

DOWN

1 Customary (8)
2 Eskimo dwelling (5)
3 Ancient empire (4)
4 Large (3)
6 Vivacious (8)
8 Capital of Japan (6)
10 Additionally (4)
11 Towards the ship's rear (3)

CROSSWORD
a Day!

ACROSS
1 Dish from 12A (5)
5 Strike with a whip (4)
6 Singer, --- Jones (5)
8 Ethnic prejudice (6)
10 Love apple (6)
12 Gandhi's country (5)
13 Slick (4)
14 Holiday accommodation (5)

DOWN
1 Stipulation (9)
2 Make the sound of a lion (4)
3 Herb (5)
4 Small version of a picture (9)
7 Country on Hispaniola (5)
9 Little (5)
11 In contact with (4)

CROSSWORD
a Day!

ACROSS
3 Title (4)
5 Claim (6)
6 *Heaven's* ---, film (4)
7 Custom (9)
10 Thought (4)
11 Chatter (6)
12 Outdoor function (4)

DOWN
1 Martyr (5)
2 Dessicate (9)
3 Arbitrate (9)
4 Maxim (5)
8 Area of high pressure (5)
9 Work of fiction (5)

CROSSWORD
a Day!

ACROSS
1 Writing tool (3)
3 Wagon (4)
5 Provide food (5)
6 *Shallow* ---, film (3)
8 River crossing (4)
9 Set alight (4)
11 Mountain pass (3)
13 --- *Frutti*, song (5)
14 Very skilled (5)
15 Moan at, pick at (3)

DOWN
1 Largest ocean (7)
2 Organic, wild (7)
3 Maize (4)
4 Chinese drink? (3)
6 Texan city (7)
7 Jetty (7)
10 'Let it stand' (4)
12 Aged (3)

DAY 224

CROSSWORD a Day!

ACROSS
4 Pride (3)
6 United (6)
7 Hazardous (9)
10 Economic decline (9)
12 Boundary (6)
13 Choose (3)

DOWN
1 Guard (6)
2 Sarcastic (6)
3 Essential (9)
5 Leader (4)
8 East (6)
9 Vocalist (6)
11 Wyatt ---,
US marshal (4)

DAY 225

CROSSWORD a Day!

ACROSS
1 Wicked (4)
4 Peaceful (4)
7 *Psycho* director (9)
8 Bistro (4)
10 Erode, --- away (4)
12 Colloquial (9)
13 Singer, --- Dee (4)
14 Beefcake (4)

DOWN
2 Here you are! (5)
3 Ill-gotten gains (5)
5 Love deeply (5)
6 Creator (5)
8 & 9D Film aimed at a female audience (5,5)
9 See 8D
10 *The Grapes of ---*, Steinbeck novel (5)
11 Extraterrestrial (5)

DAY 226

CROSSWORD
a Day!

ACROSS

1 Killing of a king (8)
5 Aperture (3)
6 Lament for the dead (5)
7 Beams (4)
9 Sneaky look (4)
13 Part of a shoe (5)
14 Obstacle (3)
15 Negative particle (8)

DOWN

1 --- Corman, film director (5)
2 Romany (5)
3 *Agent --- Banks*, teenage spy film (4)
4 Bird of prey (5)
8 Orchard fruit (5)
10 Fiery particle (5)
11 Donna ---, New York designer (5)
12 --- Stolz, actor (4)

CROSSWORD
a Day!

ACROSS
1 Machinery part (3)
3 Pack in (4)
5 Temporary stop (5)
6 --- Hoskins, actor (3)
8 Threesome (4)
9 Cut (4)
11 Hide the truth (3)
13 Animal (5)
14 --- Owens, athlete (5)
15 Look (3)

DOWN
1 Upper case (7)
2 E M Forster novel (7)
3 Musical symbol (4)
4 Chairman ---, Chinese leader (3)
6 Area of South-Eastern Europe (7)
7 Christen (7)
10 Unit of land area (4)
12 Anger (3)

DAY 228

CROSSWORD a Day!

ACROSS

1 *Love Actually* actress, --- Thompson (4)
3 Poetic ---, medieval Icelandic verse (4)
7 Ignited gas (5)
8 Twist (3)
9 31st October (9)
12 And not (3)
13 Robust (5)
14 Cult (4)
15 Remain, wait (4)

DOWN

2 Island nation (5)
4 Sir Arthur Conan ---, crime writer (5)
5 Nile city (5)
6 Enclave within South Africa (7)
9 Nautical command: All --- on deck! (5)
10 Melodic, expressive (5)
11 Concluded (5)

CROSSWORD
a Day!

ACROSS

- **1 & 3A** Sports day event (4)
- **3** See 1A
- **7** Herb (5)
- **8** Pilot, --- Johnson (3)
- **9** Expected (3)
- **10** Choke (3)
- **11** Film format (1,1,1)
- **13** Hole-punching tool (3)
- **14** Helicopter part (5)
- **15** Therefore (4)
- **16** Horizontal entrance to a mine (4)

DOWN

- **1 & 2D** New York comedy series (3,3,3,4)
- **2** See 1D
- **4** Got rid of (4)
- **5** First class (9)
- **6** Lineage (7)
- **12** Pull along (4)
- **13** Like a desert (4)

CROSSWORD
a Day!

ACROSS
- 1 Throng (5)
- 6 Principle, ethic (5)
- 7 Decorate (5)
- 9 *Ice Cold in* ---, film (4)
- 10 Surface of a tree (4)
- 14 Bar of gold (5)
- 15 Once more (5)
- 16 Book containing useful information (5)

DOWN
- 2 Conundrum (6)
- 3 Have supper (4)
- 4 *Oedipus* ---, play (3)
- 5 *Nightmare on --- Street*, horror film (3)
- 8 Governor, --- Schwarzenegger (6)
- 11 Circus arena (4)
- 12 & 13A Mel Gibson road movie (3,3)
- 13 See 12A

CROSSWORD
a Day!

ACROSS
1 See 4D
5 & 15A Former college (4,5)
8 & 10D Dickens novel (6,5)
9 Above (2)
11 Greeting (2)
12 Old spider's trap (6)
14 Creative toy (4)
15 See 5A

DOWN
2 Architectural style (5)
3 Moose (3)
4 & 1A Dickens novel (7,5)
6 Soldiers' shelter (7)
7 Wading bird (5)
10 See 8A
13 Yearly assembly of an organization (1,1,1)

DAY 232

CROSSWORD a Day!

ACROSS

1 Barred enclosure (4)
3 Wading bird (4)
7 Spectators (8)
9 Fastener (3)
10 Arch-enemy (7)
13 Mesh (3)
14 Central (frequencies) (8)
15 Point (4)
16 Scoff (4)

DOWN

2 Once more (5)
4 Joining (7)
5 Stalk (4)
6 Sour condiment (7)
8 Turned upside down (7)
11 Looks for (5)
12 Portent (4)

DAY 233

CROSSWORD
a Day!

ACROSS

1 Actor, --- Pacino (2)
2 Wears, unravels (5)
7 Wake (5)
8 See 4D
9 & 14A Cartoon rabbit (4,5)
10 Persian poet, --- Khayyam (4)
12 Train carriage (3)
13 --- four, fancy cake (5)
14 See 9A
15 Japanese board game (2)

DOWN

1 Form of exercise (8)
3 Carla in *Cheers*, --- Perlman (4)
4 & 8A Adversary of 9A & 14A (8,3)
5 Swiss mountain (8)
6 Liqueur made from almonds (8)
11 Pleasure drive (4)

CROSSWORD
a Day!

ACROSS

2 Harmonious
   relationship (7)
5 Marine creature (9)
7 Indian address (5)
12 Determination (9)
14 Area of trees
   grown for cutting (7)

DOWN

1 Ski slope (5)
2 Alex Haley book (5)
3 Doctorate (2,1)
4 Geoffrey ---,
   Shine actor (4)
6 American security
   organization (1,1,1)
8 Be ill (3)
9 David ---, singer (5)
10 Infection (5)
11 Storage tower (4)
13 21st Greek letter (3)

SOLUTION FOR DAY 233

Across 1. Al 2. Frays 7. Rouse 8. Sam 9. Bugs 10. Omar 12. Car 13. Petit 14. Bunny 15. Spin **Down** 1. Aerobics 3. Rhea 4. Yosemite 5. Jungfrau 6. Amaretto 11. Spin

CROSSWORD a Day!

ACROSS

1 Youngster (5)
3 High card (3)
6 Function, purpose (3)
7 & 11A Tibetan leader (5,4)
9 Singer, --- Fitzgerald (4)
11 See 7A
13 Snake (3)
14 Word shouted to shock people (3)
15 Range of knowledge (3)
16 Broken piece of glass (5)

DOWN

1 Make happen (5)
4 Amulet (5)
5 --- Field, actress (5)
8 Tower built to reach Heaven, and which ended in chaos (5)
10 Beaver's home (5)
12 Keep away from (5)

CROSSWORD
a Day!

ACROSS

1 Era of a nineteenth-century queen (9)
6 Non-rigid airship (5)
7 Small bulb (1,1,1)
8 White bird (4)
10 Remain (4)
13 Morning moisture (3)
14 Mixture of metals (5)
15 Put a stop to (9)

DOWN

2 Spouse's parent (2-3)
3 Word that one says after a mistake (4)
4 Small arm of the sea (5)
5 Enid Blyton character (5)
8 See 9D
9 & 8D Egyptian President 1970-1981 (5,5)
11 Fail (5)
12 West African country (4)

CROSSWORD
a Day!

ACROSS
1 Breathe heavily (4)
3 Skilled (4)
6 Norwegian money (5)
7 Norse god (3)
8 Conjuring dexterity, --- of hand (7)
13 Raincoat (3)
14 Natural sweetener (5)
15 24 hour periods (4)
16 Zesty taste (4)

DOWN
1 Voracious fish (4)
2 Overwrought (5)
4 Set of items (5)
5 Irish republic (4)
9 *Cagney and ---*, cop series (5)
10 Low guttural sound (5)
11 In the course of (4)
12 Rugged rock (4)

CROSSWORD a Day!

ACROSS
1 Bonnie's accomplice (5)
4 Young goat (3)
5 Do a practice run (8)
7 North African Muslim? (4)
8 Identical sibling (4)
11 Blood cell (8)
13 Church bench (3)
14 Stationed (5)

DOWN
1 Metal (6)
2 Rude person (from Gulliver's Travels) (5)
3 Dutch cheese (4)
4 Greek island (3)
6 Conjoined (6)
9 British principality (5)
10 End of a cigarette (4)
12 Depressed (3)

CROSSWORD
a Day!

ACROSS
1 Amount (8)
5 *Much --- About Nothing*, play (3)
6 Greek epic poem (5)
7 Fencing sword (4)
9 Bringer of bad luck (4)
13 Drinking vessel (5)
14 Hostelry (3)
15 Herb (8)

DOWN
1 Tremor (5)
2 Sun-dried brick (5)
3 Duplicate copy (4)
4 Hanker (5)
8 Aviator (5)
10 Cake topping (5)
11 Inert gas (5)
12 Employer (4)

CROSSWORD a Day!

DAY 240

ACROSS

1 Recess in a coastline (5)
4 Ruminant animal (3)
6 Gratuity (5)
8 Moan pathetically (5)
12 Area (4)
13 Affectations (4)
14 Analyze (5)
17 Drenched (3)
19 Ceramic container (3)
20 German submarine (1-4)

DOWN

1 Small part (3)
2 Cheat, swindle (3)
3 Pull behind a car (3)
4 Ho --- Minh City, Saigon (3)
5 Grief, distress (3)
7 Jeremy ---, actor (5)
9 Humorous deception (4)
10 Boldness (5)
11 Catherine --- (3)
14 Jones, actress (4)
15 Harden (3)
16 Thee (3)
17 Court (3)
18 Expression of contempt (3)

LAGOON BOOKS

CROSSWORD
a Day!

ACROSS
1. Continent (4)
3. Johann Sebastian ---, composer (4)
7. Home of The Beatles (9)
8. Stone ---, period of prehistory (3)
10. Diminutive breed (3)
12. Playwright (9)
13. Consumes (4)
14. Head (4)

DOWN
2. Wasp's weapon! (5)
4. Overhead (5)
5. Actress, --- Hunter (5)
6. Billy ---, actor (7)
8. Tennis player, --- Agassi (5)
9. Praise highly (5)
11. Start (5)

CROSSWORD a Day!

ACROSS

1 Greek hero (4)
3 Steffi ---, tennis player (4)
7 Tin for powdered tobacco (5,3)
9 As well (3)
10 *Lucky ---*, novel (3)
14 Cocktail, --- sling (3)
15 Prickly animal (8)
16 By --- of, by means of (4)
17 Jesus' mother (4)

DOWN

2 Argonauts' leader (5)
4 Red jewel (4)
5 Cunning (4)
6 Rank of soldier (7)
8 & 14D Forbidden (2,2)
11 Something to smoke (5)
12 Piece punched out of a ballot paper (4)
13 Thor's father (4)
14 See 8D

CROSSWORD a Day!

ACROSS
1 Small falcon (5)
3 Flightless bird (3)
6 Possesses (4)
7 John ---, fish (4)
8 Story of a life (9)
13 6th June 1944 (1-3)
14 Saga (4)
15 Sixth sense (3)
16 Triangular estuary (5)

DOWN
1 Nuclear weapon (1-4)
2 *Bedtime for ---*, film (5)
4 Variant form (5)
5 Concept (4)
9 Asian river (5)
10 Men (4)
11 Eye part (5)
12 Plant (5)

DAY 244

CROSSWORD a Day!

ACROSS
1. Spanish red wine (5)
5. Aromatic plant (4)
8. Yellow bird (6)
9. & 11A Kill (2,2)
11. See 9A
12. Fireplace (6)
14. Bride's headgear (4)
15. Sugary (5)

DOWN
2. Express views (5)
3. Actress, --- Basinger (3)
4. Waste away (7)
6. Earn (7)
7. Emerald, eg (5)
10. Put pen to paper (5)
13. Twitch (3)

CROSSWORD a Day!

ACROSS
1 Collapse (8)
6 Wandering singer (8)
8 Genuine (4)
9 Snooty person (4)
12 Homonym (8)
14 --- *Book*, William the Conqueror's English record (8)

DOWN
2 First animal in space (5)
3 Allocation (4)
4 Strife (3)
5 Model of the Earth (5)
7 Inebriated (5)
10 Nude (5)
11 Emerald ---, Ireland (4)
13 Chinese statesman, --- Zedong (3)

DAY 246

CROSSWORD
a Day!

ACROSS
1 Trouble (7)
6 Seep (4)
8 Abundant (4)
11 Senseless (5)
12 Windows to the soul! (4)
14 Not in use (4)
15 Dive (7)

DOWN
2 Cereal (3)
3 Away (3)
4 Group of boar (7)
5 Group of jellyfish (7)
7 Another name for the Congo River (5)
9 Turn over (5)
10 Outlaw (3)
13 Mayday (1,1,1)
14 Anger (3)

CROSSWORD
a Day!

ACROSS
1 Employed (4)
3 Request (solemnly) (4)
7 Body frame (8)
9 Life force (3)
10 Bland (7)
13 At present (3)
14 Plinth (8)
15 Type of wrestling (4)
16 Lean (4)

DOWN
2 Japanese dish (5)
4 Greek wine (7)
5 Pull (4)
6 Oval (7)
8 Territory (7)
11 Gives (out) (5)
12 Mimics (4)

CROSSWORD
a Day!

ACROSS
1 Wig (9)
6 Find the answer to (5)
7 Mend (an injury) (4)
9 Cinema employee (5)
10 Nordic letter (4)
12 Clean (plumage) (5)
13 Explosive (9)

DOWN
2 Fundamental particle (4)
3 Study for a test (6)
4 Keen (5)
5 --- Dickinson, poet (5)
7 Biblical language (6)
8 Convey (5)
9 Workers' organization (5)
11 Hereditary unit (4)

CROSSWORD a Day!

ACROSS
1 Connected by membrane (feet) (6)
6 Comfort (4)
7 Play, gambol (6)
9 Escort (9)
11 Line on a weather map (6)
12 Indication (4)
13 Respond (6)

DOWN
2 Printing mistakes (6)
3 Dancer (9)
4 Type of tree that sheds leaves annually (9)
5 Zodiac sign (3)
8 Anger (6)
10 Burnt remains (3)

CROSSWORD a Day!

ACROSS
3 Good day! (5)
6 Of the mouth (4)
7 Draining utensil (5)
8 Turn down (6)
10 Beast (6)
11 Representation (5)
12 One time (4)
13 Comedienne, --- DeGeneres (5)

DOWN
1 Biting, caustic (9)
2 --- Paterson, *Waltzing Matilda* writer (5)
4 Way out (4)
5 Wake up late (9)
7 View (5)
9 Amidst (5)
10 Feverish illness (4)

CROSSWORD a Day!

ACROSS
5 Boundless (9)
7 Aided (6)
9 Chess piece (6)
12 Witness (9)

DOWN
1 A to Z (8)
2 Little (5)
3 Eye irritation (4)
4 Spider's snare (3)
6 House shoes (8)
8 Linked metal (5)
10 Flower (4)
11 Greek letter (3)

CROSSWORD
a Day!

ACROSS
1 Writer, --- Thomas (5)
5 Singing voice (4)
6 Nimble (5)
8 Catch (6)
10 Type of cloud (6)
12 Spooky (5)
13 With capability (4)
14 Chief (ballerina) (5)

DOWN
1 Severe (9)
2 Car part (4)
3 Dally with, philander (5)
4 Ongoing TV series (4,5)
7 Follow on (5)
9 Facial expression (5)
11 Cauterize, brand (4)

SOLUTION FOR DAY 251

Across 5. Limitless 7. Helped 9. Bishop 12. Testifier
Down 1. Alphabet 2. Small 3. Stye 4. Slippers 6. Web 8. Chain 10. Iris 11. Psi

DAY 253

CROSSWORD a Day!

ACROSS
3 Light (4)
5 Cake (6)
6 Whirring sound (4)
7 Tiny spark (9)
10 Heroic story (4)
11 Papal ambassador (6)
12 Parody (4)

DOWN
1 Leers (5)
2 Accused (9)
3 Oil, eg (9)
4 Lesson of a story (5)
8 Split (5)
9 Hate (5)

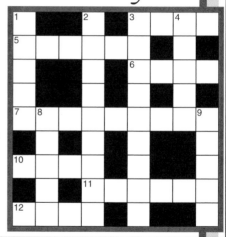

CROSSWORD
a Day!

ACROSS
1 Meeting place (5)
6 State of disgrace (5)
7 Smell (5)
8 Prediction cards (5)
9 Alloy (5)
12 Plant stem (5)
13 Cowboy contest (5)
14 Unit of heat (5)

DOWN
1 Young horse (4)
2 North American river (3,6)
3 Trench (4)
4 Low esteem (9)
5 Sooty stain (4)
9 --- Reynolds, actor (4)
10 Small drink (4)
11 Islamic prayer leader (4)

SOLUTION FOR DAY 253

Across 3. Gateau 6. Burr 7. Scintilla 10. Saga 11. Nuncio 12. Skit **Down** 1. Ogles 2. Defendant 3. Lubricant 4. Moral 8. Crack 9. Abhor

CROSSWORD
a Day!

ACROSS
1 Period before Easter (4)
3 Gulp (4)
7 Journeying leisurely (8)
9 Mathematical curve (3)
10 Close (3)
14 Film about a boy and his pet bird (3)
15 Remaining person (8)
16 Red gem (4)
17 Merchant ship officer (4)

DOWN
2 Non-speaking cast member (5)
4 Prolonged cry of distress (4)
5 Jokes (4)
6 Cut-out for applying designs to walls (7)
8 *The* ---, TV series (1,1)
11 French cap (5)
12 Employer (4)
13 Dull (4)
14 Finishing blow (1,1)

SOLUTION FOR DAY 254

Across 1. Forum 6. Odium 7. Aroma 8. Tarot 9. Brass 12. Haulm 13. Rodeo 14. Therm
Down 1. Foal 2. Rio Grande 3. Moat 4. Disrepute 5. Smut 9. Burt 10. Shot 11. Imam

CROSSWORD a Day!

ACROSS

1 Spanish city (9)
6 Director, --- Lee (5)
7 On behalf of (3)
8 Crooked (4)
10 Team of staff (4)
13 Wonder (3)
14 Goods (5)
15 Morning tea break (9)

DOWN

2 Fruit (5)
3 Balanced (4)
4 Proposal (5)
5 Missile fired from a bow (5)
8 William ---, poet (5)
9 Sibling's daughter (5)
11 Bird of prey (5)
12 Dull pain (4)

LAGOON
BOOKS

DAY 257

CROSSWORD
a Day!

ACROSS
1 Videogame lever (8)
5 Michael J --- , actor (3)
6 Pixie-like (5)
7 Additionally (4)
9 Toboggan (4)
13 Teenage worry (5)
14 Small cake (3)
15 Move abroad (8)

DOWN
1 Sterile orange (5)
2 Vertical direction in which co-ordinates are plotted (1-4)
3 *Star* ---, sci-fi film series (4)
4 Machete, eg (5)
8 Sword thrust (5)
10 Constellation (5)
11 Packed tight (5)
12 Male deer (4)

DAY 258

ACROSS
1 Shrewd (6)
6 To raise (4)
7 Wander (6)
9 Washing machine, eg (9)
11 Fastened (6)
12 Legendary (4)
13 --- Hemingway, writer (6)

DOWN
2 Irritable (6)
3 Wobble (9)
4 Height (9)
5 Greek letter (3)
8 Way in (6)
10 Beverage (3)

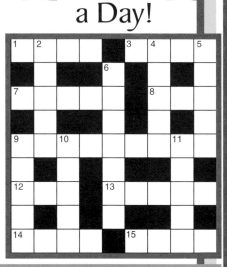

DAY 259

CROSSWORD a Day!

ACROSS

1 Website language (1,1,1,1)
3 Unfeeling (4)
7 Personal saying (5)
8 Film, --- *Weeks Notice* (3)
9 Person devoted to enjoyment (9)
12 Muhammad ---, boxer (3)
13 Cartoon character, --- Duck (5)
14 Roman garment (4)
15 Physically attractive (4)

DOWN

2 Baboon group (5)
4 Loosen, undo (5)
5 *Mrs ---*, film (5)
6 Round building (7)
9 Make law (5)
10 Bonus, --- on the cake (5)
11 Attach (5)

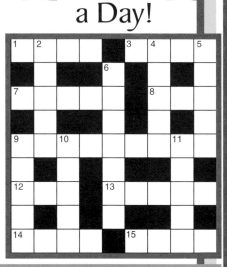

CROSSWORD
a Day!

ACROSS

1 Marine mammal (4)
3 Suspend (4)
7 Aberdeen ---,
   cattle breed (5)
8 Weapon (3)
9 Mineral source (3)
10 Introverted (3)
11 Greek god (3)
13 Harry Potter's bird (3)
14 Help, benefit (5)
15 Snake-like fish (4)
16 Oral poet (4)

DOWN

1 Island nation (9)
2 Actor, --- Rickman (4)
4 As well (4)
5 Island nation (9)
6 Boffin (7)
12 Finger part (4)
13 Gymnast,
    --- Korbut (4)

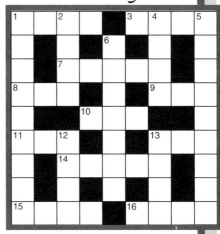

DAY 261

CROSSWORD
a Day!

ACROSS
1 John Logie ---, TV inventor (5)
6 Without company (5)
7 & 9A & 8D Leonardo DiCaprio and Tom Hanks film (5,2,2,3,3)
9 See 7A
10 Exhale (4)
14 Leave the egg (5)
15 Paris river (5)
16 Amusing (5)

DOWN
2 Rouse (6)
3 Roald ---, author (4)
4 Fight in the ring (3)
5 Fossilized wood (3)
8 See 7A
11 Cook (4)
12 Volcano product (3)
13 Dance (3)

CROSSWORD
a Day!

ACROSS
1. Waterfowl (4)
5. Corn (5)
7. Alien (7)
8. Contemporary (7)
11. Hug (7)
13. Worth (5)
14. Arrangement (4)

DOWN
1. Foolhardy (4)
2. Merry-go-round (8)
3. Fabric container (3)
4. Hundredth of a dollar (4)
5. Minute organism (7)
6. Flood, overwhelm (8)
9. Kevin Kline film (4)
10. Touch (4)
12. Wet earth (3)

CROSSWORD a Day!

ACROSS
1 Crustacean (7)
6 Himalayan animal (3)
7 Real (7)
8 Lichen (4)
9 Breed of terrier (4)
12 Pupil, learner (7)
14 Expression of surprise (3)
15 Skin pigment (7)

DOWN
1 Ship's record (3)
2 Skeleton (5)
3 The thing here (4)
4 Cereal (3)
5 Flatfish (5)
8 African grassland area, --- Mara (5)
10 Calvin ---, designer (5)
11 Boring (4)
12 Uncle ---, American personification (3)
13 Browning of skin (3)

DAY 264

CROSSWORD
a Day!

ACROSS
1 For example (1,1)
2 Thinking organ (5)
7 1980s series, *The --- of Hazzard* (5)
8 Sphere (3)
9 Surprise attack (4)
10 See 5D
12 Musical note (3)
13 Least good (5)
14 Money-lending (5)
15 Exist (2)

DOWN
1 Legendary city (2,6)
3 Trick (4)
4 Worship of false gods (8)
5 & 10A Heath Ledger film (1,7,4)
6 Missing person (8)
11 Pitcher (4)

DAY 265

CROSSWORD
a Day!

ACROSS
- 2 Waterfall (7)
- 5 Youth (9)
- 7 Wear away (5)
- 12 Green nut (9)
- 14 Song, --- *Wizard* (7)

DOWN
- 1 Sailing boat (5)
- 2 Michael ---, actor (5)
- 3 Depressed (3)
- 4 Grim fate (4)
- 6 Concealed (3)
- 8 Deep track made by wheels (3)
- 9 Actress, --- Merman (5)
- 10 Die in water (5)
- 11 Very small (4)
- 13 Actress, --- Gardner (3)

CROSSWORD
a Day!

ACROSS

1 Extent (4)
3 Summit (4)
7 Sailing sport (8)
9 Assent (3)
10 Moral (7)
13 Weapon (3)
14 Mathematical statement (8)
15 Fashion (4)
16 Reverberation (4)

DOWN

2 Receiver of money (5)
4 Windy city (7)
5 Rim (4)
6 --- Turlington, model (7)
8 Amaze (7)
11 Midday meal (5)
12 Smile radiantly (4)

CROSSWORD
a Day!

ACROSS
1 Large formal band (9)
6 Shaver (5)
7 Battle, crusade (3)
8 Distant sun (4)
10 Killer whale (4)
13 Bolt accompaniment (3)
14 Pseudonym (5)
15 Working animal (9)

DOWN
2 Respond (5)
3 Work for money (4)
4 Tall structure (5)
5 Main artery (5)
8 Using sound (5)
9 Performer (5)
11 Social level (5)
12 Sprint (4)

CROSSWORD
a Day!

ACROSS
1 Extremity (4)
3 --- O'Brien, writer (4)
6 Partner (5)
7 Caribbean spirit (3)
8 Précis (7)
13 Cancelled (3)
14 Long-legged bird (5)
15 Chomp (4)
16 Holy cross (4)

DOWN
1 Grasp (4)
2 Nocturnal reverie (5)
4 Albrecht ---,
German engraver (5)
5 Military force (4)
9 Out of shape (5)
10 Moving (5)
11 Haircare item (4)
12 Derelict area,
--- row (4)

LAGOON BOOKS

DAY 269

CROSSWORD
a Day!

ACROSS
1 Evade (5)
4 Inlet (3)
5 Area of France (8)
7 Type of metal (4)
8 Winter precipitation (4)
11 Southern state (8)
13 Soft muddy ground (3)
14 Avarice (5)

DOWN
1 & 2A Jake Gyllenhaal film (6,5)
2 See 1A
3 Dutch cheese (4)
4 Unopened flower (3)
6 Persuaded (6)
9 Unexploited market (5)
10 Buck (4)
12 Easter treat (3)

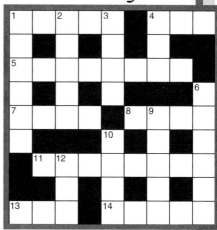

DAY 270

CROSSWORD
a Day!

ACROSS
3 Entice (5)
6 Piece of furniture (5)
7 Drivers' accommodation (5)
8 Stun, amaze (7)
12 Myanmar (5)
14 Ancient fragment (5)
15 Foe (5)

DOWN
1 Hide on board, --- away (4)
2 Chasm (5)
3 Non-permanent (9)
4 Encountered (3)
5 Of great height (4)
9 Principled (5)
10 Competent (4)
11 Ship's floor (4)
13 Deer species (3)

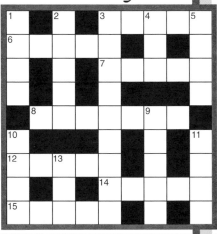

CROSSWORD
a Day!

ACROSS
1 Remain (4)
3 Egyptian goddess (4)
7 Many (8)
9 Writing implement (3)
10 Grazes (7)
13 Pointed end (3)
14 Steer (8)
15 Healthy (4)
16 Worry (4)

DOWN
2 Domesticates (5)
4 Wise (7)
5 Prophet (4)
6 Bizarre (7)
8 Impolite (7)
11 Blockade (5)
12 Chew (4)

DAY 272

CROSSWORD a Day!

ACROSS

1 Spend money (4)
3 Comic genius, --- Laurel (4)
7 US city (9)
8 Ingested (3)
10 Maiden name indicator (3)
12 Robert Louis Stevenson novel (9)
13 Function (4)
14 Encryption (4)

DOWN

2 Haul up (5)
4 Superficial (gesture) (5)
5 Relative (5)
6 Iraqi capital (7)
8 Misaligned (5)
9 Tree (5)
11 Correct (5)

CROSSWORD a Day!

ACROSS

1 Kitchen appliance (4)
3 Raise (4)
7 Bedtime drink (8)
9 Stop filming! (3)
10 Undercover agent (3)
14 Friend (3)
15 See 2D
16 Flat boat (4)
17 Prepare food (4)

DOWN

2 & 15A Tennis star (5,8)
4 Small distance (4)
5 Category (4)
6 Charlie ---, silent film star (7)
8 Computer systems (1,1)
11 Lariat (5)
12 Exchange (4)
13 Quiche (4)
14 In the afternoon (1,1)

CROSSWORD
a Day!

ACROSS
1 May (5)
3 Parched (3)
6 Spirit, heart (4)
7 Makes a sum (4)
8 Shore (9)
13 Financial institution (4)
14 Check text (4)
15 Painting, eg (3)
16 Dog breed (5)

DOWN
1 Tune (5)
2 Dutch cheese (5)
4 *The Kiss* sculptor (5)
5 Entrance corridor (4)
9 Broadcasting (2,3)
10 Rice wine (4)
11 First (finger) (5)
12 Take part in (a competition) (5)

CROSSWORD a Day!

ACROSS

1 Long-nosed animal (8)
5 Racket (3)
6 Repetitive song (5)
7 Outbuilding (4)
9 Chief (4)
13 Debate (5)
14 Boundary (3)
15 French leader (8)

DOWN

1 Mountain range (5)
2 Wash lightly (5)
3 Moral weakness (4)
4 African republic (5)
8 Wading bird (5)
10 Spooky (5)
11 Evil spirit (5)
12 Fiddling Emperor! (4)

CROSSWORD a Day!

ACROSS
- 1 School assignment (8)
- 6 Show to be false (8)
- 8 Pursued animal (4)
- 9 Footwear (4)
- 12 Handle, moniker (8)
- 14 Lawyer (8)

DOWN
- 2 US state (5)
- 3 Clean with a cloth (4)
- 4 Kanga's baby in Winnie-the-Pooh (3)
- 5 Postpone (5)
- 7 Buy things (5)
- 10 Person (5)
- 11 Useful data (4)
- 13 Moggy (3)

CROSSWORD a Day!

ACROSS

1 & 15A H G Wells novel (3,4,7)
6 Insect (4)
8 Part of an egg (4)
11 Livid (5)
12 Pay attention to (4)
14 Window frame (4)
15 See 1A

DOWN

2 Largest deer (3)
3 Climbing plant (3)
4 Embassy employee (7)
5 Rough (7)
7 Herb (5)
9 Greek letter (5)
10 Animal's mother (3)
13 One of Snow White's dwarfs (3)
14 Exercise on snow (3)

DAY 278

CROSSWORD
a Day!

ACROSS
1 Yemen port (4)
3 Explosive device (4)
7 User (8)
9 Island in Indian Ocean (3)
10 Motto (7)
13 Tree (3)
14 Insolvent (8)
15 Circular tent (4)
16 Sandhill (4)

DOWN
2 Wilt (5)
4 Rock formation (7)
5 Submerge, sink (4)
6 Courage (7)
8 Companion (7)
11 Conductor's aide (5)
12 Follow instructions (4)

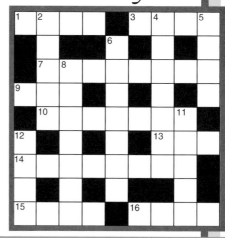

CROSSWORD
a Day!

ACROSS
1. Full-time manager of home affairs (9)
6. Intimidating person (5)
7. Sugar source (4)
9. Medium male voice (5)
10. Vegetable (4)
12. Bend over (5)
13. Thrill, invigorate (9)

DOWN
2. Burden (4)
3. Internal organ (6)
4. Entomb (5)
5. Vacant (5)
7. Rigid straw hat (6)
8. Treat demeaningly (5)
9. Style preference (5)
11. Horse's foot (4)

CROSSWORD a Day!

ACROSS
1 *Wind in the Willows* character (6)
6 Obtain by work (4)
7 Courageous (6)
9 Carving on whalebone (9)
11 Hanging frozen water (6)
12 On one occasion (4)
13 Indicate (6)

DOWN
2 Business serving others (6)
3 Exalted (9)
4 Reduction in trade (9)
5 Small insect (3)
8 Secret vote (6)
10 Came first (3)

CROSSWORD
a Day!

ACROSS
3 Buddhist shrine (5)
6 Chamber (4)
7 Seasonal decrease in prices (5)
8 French Polynesian island (6)
10 Confused din (6)
11 Fool (5)
12 Yemen port (4)
13 Hillbilly (5)

DOWN
1 Cruelty (9)
2 Fine coffee (5)
4 Siamese? (4)
5 Able to take in water (9)
7 Fat (5)
9 Hymn, --- *With Me* (5)
10 Space (4)

SOLUTION FOR DAY 280

Across 1. Badger 6. Earn 7. Heroic 9. Scrimshaw 11. Icicle 12. Once 13. Denote
Down 2. Agency 3. Glorified 4. Recession 5. Ant 8. Ballot 10. Won

CROSSWORD a Day!

ACROSS
5 Correction (9)
7 Concoct (6)
9 Take (6)
12 Eradicate (9)

DOWN
1 Changeable (8)
2 Gusto (5)
3 First garden? (4)
4 Turkish cap (3)
6 Unlucky number! (8)
8 Commemorative disc (6)
10 Wind in loops (4)
11 Sewing aid (3)

LAGOON BOOKS

DAY 283

CROSSWORD a Day!

ACROSS
1 Flower from Amsterdam! (5)
5 Adhesive (4)
6 Constellation of the Ram (5)
8 Horseriding equipment (6)
10 Number (6)
12 Boredom (5)
13 Perform a ditty (4)
14 Mike ---, boxer (5)

DOWN
1 Permeate (9)
2 Finishes (a cake) (4)
3 Fly without power (5)
4 Welcome (9)
7 Fencing sword (5)
9 Representative (5)
11 Covetousness (4)

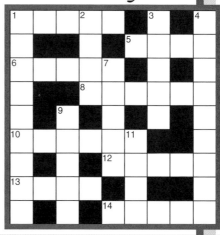

DAY 284

CROSSWORD a Day!

ACROSS
3 Sensitivity (4)
5 Consent to (6)
6 Edward ---, poet (4)
7 Abducted (9)
10 --- of March, bad day for Caesar (4)
11 Old name for China (6)
12 Shaft (4)

DOWN
1 Textile design (5)
2 Remember (9)
3 Zoom (lens) (9)
4 Moving platform (5)
8 List of items (5)
9 --- Hannah actress (5)

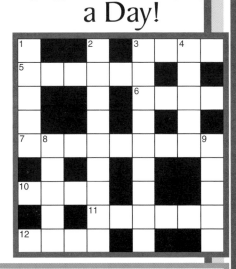

SOLUTION FOR DAY 283

Across 1. Tulip 5. Glue 6. Aries 8. Saddle 10. Figure 12. Ennui 13. Sing 14. Tyson
Down 1. Transfuse 2. Ices 3. Glide 4. Receotion 7. Sabre 9. Agent 11. Envy

DAY 285

CROSSWORD a Day!

ACROSS
1 Wanderer (5)
6 Loosen (5)
7 Titled peer (5)
8 Type of glazed earthenware (5)
9 French impressionist painter (5)
12 Employment (5)
13 South African grassland (5)
14 Overturn (5)

DOWN
1 Skating arena (4)
2 Spiritedly (9)
3 Regretted (4)
4 Impasse (9)
5 Path or strip (4)
9 Displace (4)
10 Ballet skirt (4)
11 Tear violently (4)

DAY 286

CROSSWORD a Day!

ACROSS
4 Purchase (3)
6 Attraction (6)
7 Deserted (9)
10 Cad (9)
12 Tackiness (6)
13 Some (3)

DOWN
1 Pester (6)
2 West Texas city (2,4)
3 Wisely (9)
5 Desire (4)
8 Conventional (6)
9 Mellifluous (6)
11 Maize (4)

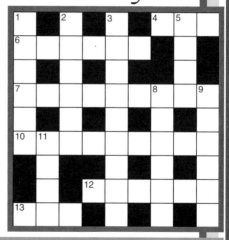

CROSSWORD
a Day!

ACROSS
1. Miss out (4)
4. *Waterloo* band (4)
7. Gaming equipment with a bullseye (9)
8. Washing tub (4)
10. Grain husks (4)
12. Day of the week (9)
13. Coarse file (4)
14. Shipping canal (4)

DOWN
2. Marsupial (5)
3. Vegetable-growing area (5)
5. British PM (5)
6. W H ---, writer (5)
8. Secluded place in a garden (5)
9. *The Prince of* ---, film (5)
10. Foundation (5)
11. Maxim (5)

DAY 288

CROSSWORD
a Day!

ACROSS
1 John ---, actor (5)
3 Pretence (3)
6 Gorilla, eg (3)
7 Human chattel (5)
9 Urban settlement (4)
11 Standard (4)
13 Chat show host, --- Springer (5)
14 Flying mammal (3)
15 *Howard's* ---, E M Forster novel (3)
16 Germaine ---, writer (5)

DOWN
1 Recite rhythmically (5)
4 Put the lid on (5)
5 Throw (5)
8 Breathe noisily in sleep (5)
10 Large sea (5)
12 Engine (5)

DAY 289

CROSSWORD a Day!

ACROSS
1. Successful record (3)
3. 50% (4)
5. Person over 18 (5)
6. Lever (open) (3)
8. Dirt (4)
9. From Helsinki? (4)
11. Edible tuber (3)
13. Astonish (5)
14. Sucking creature (5)
15. Agreed! (3)

DOWN
1. Gossip (7)
2. Holiday industry (7)
3. Detest (4)
4. Distant (3)
6. Main, principal (7)
7. NY baseball team (7)
10. Whack (4)
12. *We --- Family*, Sister Sledge hit (3)

CROSSWORD
a Day!

ACROSS
1 Operates (4)
3 Cain's brother (4)
7 Large (jet) (5)
8 & 10D Film, --- *Station* --- (3,5)
9 Idler (9)
12 Baby wolf (3)
13 Backless chair (5)
14 Baked bread (4)
15 Nourish (4)

DOWN
2 Underwater apparatus (5)
4 *Life of ---*, film (5)
5 Ogles (5)
6 Kenyan port (7)
9 In the vicinity (5)
10 See 8A
11 Induce (emotions) (5)

CROSSWORD a Day!

ACROSS

1 House rodent (5)
6 Fruit (5)
7 Source of power for early trains (5)
9 Written collection (4)
10 Clock face (4)
14 *The Wind in the Willows* character (5)
15 Snake (5)
16 Tent (5)

DOWN

2 Costume (6)
3 US TV award (4)
4 High explosive (3)
5 Film, --- *Story* (3)
8 Fortress (6)
11 Obnoxious child (4)
12 Perform (3)
13 *Star Wars* character, --- Wan Kenobe (3)

CROSSWORD
a Day!

ACROSS
1 Long seat (5)
6 Overweight (5)
7 Noble gas (5)
9 Lithe (4)
10 University courtyard (4)
14 Suspicion (5)
15 Knight's weapon (5)
16 Direction (5)

DOWN
2 Continent (6)
3 Sharpen (4)
4 --- Kingsley, actor (3)
5 Clothes hook (3)
8 Lucky character (6)
11 At what time (4)
12 Everyone (3)
13 Wildebeest (3)

CROSSWORD
a Day!

ACROSS
1 Area around the throat (4)
5 Valuable possession (5)
7 Pilot's area (7)
8 Amiable (7)
11 Hallowed (7)
13 Islamic ruling (5)
14 Given birth to (4)

DOWN
1 Bottle part (4)
2 Conscientious objector (8)
3 Greek letter (3)
4 Salt Lake state (4)
5 Loss of speech (7)
6 High heel (8)
9 Sinister side? (4)
10 Blue-green (4)
12 Amazement (3)

CROSSWORD
a Day!

ACROSS

1 Chocolate ingredient (5)
3 Recede (3)
6 Metal (4)
7 Gaelic language (4)
8 Dutch city (9)
13 Close-fittting (4)
14 Pollution, --- rain (4)
15 Person who steers a rowing boat (3)
16 Faithful (5)

DOWN

1 Asian country (5)
2 Irritated (5)
4 Iraq's second city (5)
5 Expensive (4)
9 Juicy fruit (5)
10 Country (4)
11 Dummy used for traps (5)
12 Olympic award (5)

CROSSWORD
a Day!

ACROSS
1 Myself (2)
2 Napped (5)
7 Reigned (5)
8 Hostelry (3)
9 Jennifer ---, *Dirty Dancing* actress (4)
10 Show off (4)
12 *To Kill a Mockingbird* author, Harper --- (3)
13 Helmet part (5)
14 Dust jacket summary (5)
15 Towards the sky (2)

DOWN
1 Calendula (8)
3 Metal ore vein (4)
4 Woodland flower (8)
5 Wild hyacinth (8)
6 Winter flower (8)
11 Across to the other side (4)

CROSSWORD a Day!

ACROSS
- **2** Emit (7)
- **5** Unfortunate (9)
- **7** Con (5)
- **12** Ongoing (9)
- **14** German castle used as a prison (7)

DOWN
- **1** Wed (5)
- **2** Entitlement (5)
- **3** Decease (3)
- **4** Stretched tight (4)
- **6** Gentle attention (1,1,1)
- **8** Grass, sneak (3)
- **9** Clumsy person (5)
- **10** Containing sodium chloride (5)
- **11** Jumping stick (4)
- **13** Dictator, --- Amin (3)

CROSSWORD a Day!

ACROSS
1 Picture holder (5)
3 At this time (3)
6 Mouth part (3)
7 Doubled fold in clothing (5)
9 Urban transport (4)
11 Look, bearing (4)
13 Cost (5)
14 Atmospheric gases (3)
15 Travel in the sky (3)
16 Wonderland girl (5)

DOWN
1 Film, --- *Club* (5)
4 Give a speech (5)
5 Hold responsible (5)
8 Peasant's top (5)
10 Of the countryside (5)
12 Medieval Norwegian language (5)

CROSSWORD
a Day!

ACROSS
1 Amnesiac (9)
6 Prepare (dough) (5)
7 Alien spacecraft (1,1,1)
8 Arboreal plant (4)
10 Richard ---, actor (4)
13 Baseball hitter (3)
14 Possibly (5)
15 Disappear into the air (9)

DOWN
2 Person in possession (5)
3 Small whirlpool (4)
4 *The Magic* ---, opera (5)
5 Unconfined (5)
8 Set of data (5)
9 Supplementary (5)
11 Android (5)
12 Bullets (4)

SOLUTION FOR DAY 297

Across 1. Frame 3. Now 6. Gum 7. Pleat 9. Tram 11. Mien 13. Price 14. Air 15. Fly 16. Alice **Down** 1. *Fight* 4. Orate 5. Smock 8. Blame 10. Rural 12. Norse

CROSSWORD
a Day!

ACROSS
1 Hand over (4)
3 Cigarette end (4)
6 Beg (5)
7 Biblical vessel (3)
8 Film, --- *Choice* (7)
13 Animation (1,1,1)
14 Unwanted metal (5)
15 Number of
   a cat's lives (4)
16 Rant (4)

DOWN
1 Smoking
   implement (4)
2 Raised note (5)
4 Industry (5)
5 Child's vehicle (4)
9 Vegetable (5)
10 Become subject to (5)
11 Medical procedure (4)
12 Iridescent gem (4)

CROSSWORD
a Day!

ACROSS

1 Internet connection equipment (5)
4 Knock lightly (3)
5 Slanting (8)
7 Ogle (4)
8 Water (4)
11 Barren (8)
13 Take to court (3)
14 Laughing animal? (5)

DOWN

1 Interfere (6)
2 Elizabethan explorer, Sir Francis --- (5)
3 Frame of mind (4)
4 Beverage (3)
6 Photographic equipment (6)
9 Tremble (5)
10 Flying insect (4)
12 Lamb's mother (3)

SOLUTION FOR DAY 299

Across 1. Pass 3. Stub 6. Plead 7. Ark 8. *Sophie's* 13. CGI 14. Scrap 15. Nine 16. Rail
Down 1. Pipe 2. Sharp 4. Trade 5. Bike 9. Onion 10. Incur 11. Scan 12. Opal

DAY 301

CROSSWORD a Day!

ACROSS
3 Din (5)
6 Hot drink (5)
7 Heart membrane (5)
8 Rearranged letters (7)
12 Skin transplant (5)
14 Many a time (5)
15 Dissuade (5)

DOWN
1 Excelled in (a test) (4)
2 Ridicule (5)
3 Guide, pilot (9)
4 Afflicted (3)
5 Regular (4)
9 Blood vessel (5)
10 Added years to (4)
11 Magical baton (4)
13 Towards an aircraft's tail (3)

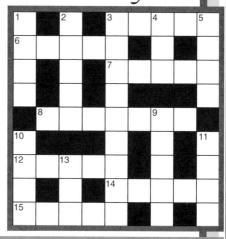

CROSSWORD
a Day!

ACROSS
1 Wallop (5)
4 Drink a little (3)
6 Fellow (3)
8 Crustacean (5)
12 Worry (4)
13 Part of the leg (4)
14 Garden figure (5)
17 Continued overleaf (1,1,1)
19 By now (3)
20 Military equipment (5)

DOWN
1 Tennis player,
 --- Henman (3)
2 Vase (3)
3 Seed (3)
4 Marine area (3)
5 Play on words (3)
7 Cook's garment (5)
9 Remainder (4)
10 Belt area (5)
11 Stalk (4)
14 --- Richie, director (3)
15 Not to be considered (3)
16 Audio equipment (3)
17 Launch area (3)
18 Rowing blade (3)

DAY 303

CROSSWORD a Day!

ACROSS

1 Instrument (4)
3 Wading bird (4)
7 Make look foolish (9)
8 Automatic progression in a competition (3)
10 Utter (3)
12 Length of life (9)
13 Creative sphere (4)
14 Lagomorph (4)

DOWN

2 Uneven (road) (5)
4 Copper-zinc alloy (5)
5 Actress, --- Spacek (5)
6 Novel and film, --- *Jones's Diary* (7)
8 Light wood (5)
9 Max ---, surrealist (5)
11 Church feature (5)

CROSSWORD a Day!

ACROSS
1 Wild goat (4)
3 Practice boxing (4)
7 Pit (8)
9 Cut off (branches) (3)
10 Electrical unit (3)
14 Attempt (3)
15 Ridged material (8)
16 Silent performance (4)
17 Garden track (4)

DOWN
2 Francis ---, painter (5)
4 Agony (4)
5 Stink (4)
6 Greek mountain (7)
8 Surgical procedure (2)
11 Burial vault (5)
12 Residue (4)
13 Squash (in) (4)
14 *Ashes --- Ashes*, David Bowie song (2)

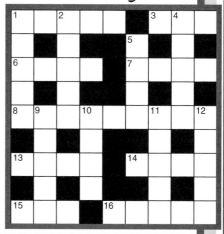

DAY 305

CROSSWORD
a Day!

ACROSS
1 Small salad plant (5)
3 Shoot with a stun gun (3)
6 Church recess (4)
7 Romantic feelings (4)
8 Tiny (9)
13 Hairless (4)
14 Dark red (4)
15 Hassidic, eg (3)
16 Give money back (5)

DOWN
1 Gorge (5)
2 German city (5)
4 Blacksmith's block (5)
5 Alliance (4)
9 Foolish (5)
10 Asian language (4)
11 Carry out a coup d'état against (5)
12 Rock used for polishing (5)

LAGOON BOOKS

SOLUTION FOR DAY 304
Across 1. Ibex 3. Spar 7. Coalmine 9. Lop 10. Amp 14. Try 15. Corduroy 16. Mime 17. Path
Down 2. Bacon 4. Pain 5. Reek 6. Olympus 8. Op 11. Crypt 12. Scum 13. Cram 14. To

CROSSWORD
a Day!

ACROSS

1 Resentment (5)
5 Billy ---, actor (4)
8 Negative renown (6)
9 --- *Better Blues*, Spike Lee film (2)
11 Indian meditation syllable (2)
12 Emotional tension (6)
14 Operatic song (4)
15 Lovers' meeting (5)

DOWN

2 Drink deeply (5)
3 Cooling device (3)
4 Regret (7)
6 Soldier's temporary camp (7)
7 Will ---, actor (5)
10 Female donkey (5)
13 Soft fruit (3)

DAY 307

CROSSWORD a Day!

ACROSS

1 Centennial state (8)
6 Largest US state (8)
8 Ancient Hindu scriptures (4)
9 Line to stand behind when playing darts (4)
12 Prairie state (8)
14 First US state (8)

DOWN

2 Scottish aristocrat (5)
3 Great anger (4)
4 Lair (3)
5 *Psycho* motel (5)
7 Singer, --- Lavigne (5)
10 Porcelain (5)
11 Film, --- *and the King* (4)
13 Falsehood (3)

DAY 308

CROSSWORD a Day!

ACROSS
1 --- Falco, *The Sopranos* actress (4)
3 Avian (4)
7 Fictional detective, --- Holmes (8)
9 & 11D Brendan Fraser film (3,5)
10 Had a meal (3)
14 Seabird (3)
15 Life form (8)
16 Part of Florida (4)
17 Toy (2-2)

DOWN
2 Gorgeous (5)
4 Effigy (4)
5 Dick Van ---, actor (4)
6 Put on an act (7)
8 That man (2)
11 See 9A
12 Piece of cutlery (4)
13 Unattractive (4)
14 Like (2)

CROSSWORD a Day!

ACROSS
1 From Edinburgh? (4)
3 'So be it' (4)
7 Spanish dance (8)
9 Indecision, --- and buts (3)
10 Hair product (7)
13 Stick one's --- in, interfere (3)
14 Chewing animal (8)
15 Manufactured (4)
16 Verdant (4)

DOWN
2 Shirt part (5)
4 Rainy season (7)
5 Gas used in lights (4)
6 Intransigent (7)
8 Guilty (7)
11 Sacred promises (5)
12 High school party (4)

CROSSWORD a Day!

ACROSS

1 Bruise (9)
6 Make amends (5)
7 Tread wearily (4)
9 Skull cavity (5)
10 Accesses (a supply) (4)
12 Baa (5)
13 As large as life (4-5)

DOWN

2 Horse food? (4)
3 Pete Sampras's sport (6)
4 False gods (5)
5 Clingy (5)
7 Communal (6)
8 Ceremonial rod (5)
9 Accidentally pour (5)
11 Bucket (4)

DAY 311

CROSSWORD a Day!

ACROSS
1 Time to be at home (6)
6 Missing from the army (4)
7 Drawing tool (6)
9 Self-control (9)
11 Portuguese city (6)
12 Generous act, --- geste (4)
13 Exercises (3-3)

DOWN
2 Irregular (6)
3 Flippant (9)
4 Aboriginal custom (9)
5 Measure of length for material (3)
8 Arch of the foot (6)
10 Stomach muscles (3)

SOLUTION FOR DAY 310
Across 1. Contusion 6. Alone 7. Plod 9. Sinus 10. Taps 12. Bleat 13. Full-scale
Down 2. Oats 3. Tennis 4. Idols 5. Needy 7. Public 8. Staff 9. Spill 11. Pail

CROSSWORD
a Day!

ACROSS

3 Scatter (5)
6 Unit of land measurement (4)
7 Riotous feast (5)
8 Sir Isaac ---, physicist (6)
10 Canal country (6)
11 Cherub, eg (5)
12 Unimprisoned (4)
13 Passionate (5)

DOWN

1 Pastime involving dye 'bullets' (9)
2 Catch fish with a deep net (5)
4 Adolescent (4)
5 Rolled room decoration (9)
7 Kingly (5)
9 Titania, eg (5)
10 Hide (4)

SOLUTION FOR DAY 311

Across 1. Curfew 6. AWOL 7. Pencil 9. Restraint 11. Oporto 12. Beau 13. Sit-ups
Down 2. Uneven 3. Facetious 4. Walkabout 5. Ell 8. Instep 10. Abs

CROSSWORD
a Day!

ACROSS
5 Cat-killing quality (9)
7 Impression (6)
9 Consist (6)
12 Of the ground (9)

DOWN
1 Mishap (8)
2 Profession (5)
3 Rhinoceros's weapon (4)
4 Set of parts (3)
6 Juvenile animal (8)
8 Message device (5)
10 Linguist and political thinker, --- Chomsky (4)
11 Joan of ---, saint (3)

CROSSWORD
a Day!

ACROSS
1 Malicious (5)
5 Couch (4)
6 Leases (5)
8 Remove bedding (6)
10 Body of water between Africa and Arabia (3,3)
12 Gun (5)
13 Let out (4)
14 Frontiersman, --- Earp (5)

DOWN
1 Gardening habitats (9)
2 South African archbishop (4)
3 Precious stone (5)
4 Soft cheese (9)
7 Show contempt (5)
9 Let in (5)
11 Breezy (4)

CROSSWORD
a Day!

ACROSS
1 Level, horizontal (4)
3 Winter sports kit (4)
7 Wire (8)
9 Cocktail, --- Royale (3)
10 Land of the free! (1,1,1)
14 Mork's planet (3)
15 Statuette (8)
16 Simon ---, game (4)
17 Spear-like weapon (4)

DOWN
2 Ancient language (5)
4 Scottish church (4)
5 Identical (4)
6 Demented (7)
8 Hospital series (1,1)
11 From Athens? (5)
12 Does away with (4)
13 *Cinderella* characters, --- Sisters (4)
14 Going ahead (2)

DAY 316

CROSSWORD a Day!

ACROSS

1 Reflected sound (4)
3 Woody plant (4)
7 Dark period (5)
8 Creative output (3)
9 *The Cat in the ---*, Dr. Seuss book (3)
10 Repair (3)
11 Science room (3)
13 Crystallize (3)
14 Radiation beam (5)
15 Notice (4)
16 Catch (4)

DOWN

1 Set up (9)
2 Seek pursue (4)
4 Biblical woman (4)
5 Human being (9)
6 Opposed to (7)
12 Film, --- *Velvet* (4)
13 Broad smile (4)

SOLUTION FOR DAY 315

Across 1. Flat 3. Skis 7. Telegram 9. Kir 10 USA 14. Ork 15. Figurine 16. Says 17. Pike
Down 2. Latin 4. Kirk 5. Same 6. Berserk 8. *ER* 11. Greek 12. Ofts 13. Ugly 14. On

CROSSWORD
a Day!

ACROSS
4 Chilly (3)
6 Articulated at the back of the throat (6)
7 Uprising (9)
10 European country (9)
12 Honoré de ---, novelist (6)
13 Yes (on a ship) (3)

DOWN
1 Minimum number for a vote (6)
2 Canadian province (6)
3 Neoclassical style of architecture (9)
5 Designer, --- Chanel (4)
8 Charge (particles) (6)
9 Subtlety (6)
11 --- Williams, crooner (4)

SOLUTION FOR DAY 316

Across 1. Echo 3. Tree 7. Night 8. Art 9. *Hat* 10. Fix 11. Lab 13. Gel 14. Laser 15. Heed 16. Snag **Down** 1. Establish 2. Ruth 4. Hunt 5. Earthling 6. Against 12. *Blue* 13. Grin

DAY 318

CROSSWORD
a Day!

ACROSS
1 Milky white stone (4)
4 Mark of injury (4)
7 Pomegranate syrup (9)
8 Actor, --- Connery (4)
10 Tiresome person (4)
12 Suit design (9)
13 Rock 'n' ---, musical style (4)
14 Holler (4)

DOWN
2 Thoroughly clear (5)
3 Soviet leader (5)
5 *The Purple Rose of* ---, film (5)
6 Historical bailiff (5)
8 Smashing (5)
9 Abolish (5)
10 Nuts (5)
11 Deflect (5)

SOLUTION FOR DAY 317

Across 4. Icy 6. Uvular 7. Rebellion 10. Macedonia 12. Balzac 13. Aye
Down 1. Quorum 2. Quebec 3. Palladian 5. Coco 8. Ionize 9. Nuance 11. Andy

CROSSWORD
a Day!

ACROSS
1 Marine mammal (7)
6 How old (3)
7 *Good ---*
   Vietnam, film (7)
8 Musical, *--- and Dolls* (4)
9 Mix (4)
12 Cicada (7)
14 Welcome garland (3)
15 Laser, radar, eg (7)

DOWN
1 Not brightly lit (3)
2 Actor, --- Hagman (5)
3 Flag down (a taxi) (4)
4 Horse (3)
5 Raise objections,
   lodge a protest (5)
8 Feeling of blame (5)
10 Coupon (5)
11 Level (4)
12 United States security
   organization (1,1,1)
13 --- Selleck, actor (3)

CROSSWORD
a Day!

ACROSS
1 Small flower (5)
6 Pacific, eg (5)
7 Critical (5)
8 Two-masted sailing vessel (5)
9 Navigate (5)
12 Unreasonable (5)
13 Concentrate (5)
14 Attuned (5)

DOWN
1 Plummet (4)
2 Understanding (9)
3 Vitellus (4)
4 The recent past (9)
5 Unit of measurement (4)
9 Light gust of air (4)
10 Elephant's tooth (4)
11 Deal (4)

DAY 321

CROSSWORD
a Day!

ACROSS
1 Prayer end (4)
3 Burn (4)
7 Flower (8)
9 Baby's accessory (3)
10 Hermit (7)
13 Help (3)
14 Gushing (8)
15 Probability (4)
16 Drill (4)

DOWN
2 Newspapers,
   TV etc (5)
4 Roman emperor (7)
5 Govern (4)
6 Influences (7)
8 Escape (7)
11 Havana, eg (5)
12 Capital
   of Norway (4)

ORD

4 5

6

13

DAY 323

CROSSWORD a Day!

ACROSS
1 Religion (5)
6 Irate (5)
7 Happening (5)
9 Seaweed jelly (4)
10 Lightning flash (4)
14 Veranda (5)
15 Acclimatize (5)
16 Geeks (5)

DOWN
2 Fierce (6)
3 Reproduce (4)
4 Hen's produce (3)
5 Fitness club (3)
8 Calm, inert (6)
11 Uninhibited (4)
12 Legal structure (3)
13 Place (3)

LAGOON BOOKS

DAY 324

CROSSWORD
a Day!

ACROSS
1 *Frasier*'s city (7)
6 Curved shape (4)
8 Heath (4)
11 See 3D
12 Offensive (4)
14 Component (4)
15 Film, --- *Gump* (7)

DOWN
2 Play, --- *My Sons* (3)
3 & 11A *Big* actor (3,5)
4 Open-air blaze (7)
5 Confidential (7)
7 Greenfly (5)
9 Actor-director, --- Welles (5)
10 TV news channel (1,1,1)
13 Be incorrect (3)
14 Take advantage of (3)

DAY 325

CROSSWORD a Day!

ACROSS
1. Bill (7)
6. Cash dispenser (1,1,1)
7. Fortune teller (7)
8. Portend (4)
9. Skin irritation (4)
12. Malaysian Borneo (7)
14. Actor's prompt (3)
15. Tracked (7)

DOWN
1. Sprite (3)
2. Just, reasonable (5)
3. Eye part (4)
4. Gobble up (3)
5. Break (5)
8. Top pool ball (5)
10. Bathroom cloth (5)
11. Constellation, --- Major (4)
12. Collection (3)
13. Baby goat (3)

CROSSWORD
a Day!

ACROSS
- 1 & 15A Phrase sung by dwarfs (2,2)
- 2 Unambiguous (5)
- 7 Spirit in *The Tempest* (5)
- 8 Raincoat (3)
- 9 Absence (4)
- 10 Buy things (4)
- 12 Grandmother (3)
- 13 Turn rapidly (5)
- 14 Sizeable (5)
- 15 See 1A

DOWN
- 1 Article title (8)
- 3 Lounge, sprawl (4)
- 4 Comfortable seat (8)
- 5 Cubic ---, fake diamond (8)
- 6 Mexican resort (8)
- 11 Drink from the bottle (4)

CROSSWORD a Day!

ACROSS
2 New Orleans (3,4)
5 Flexible (9)
7 Waste matter (5)
12 Anticlimax (4,5)
14 Book collection (7)

DOWN
1 Scarf covering the shoulders (5)
2 Weak in taste (5)
3 Belly (3)
4 Seasoning (4)
6 Beast of burden (3)
8 Tear (3)
9 Cheeky (5)
10 Thick wire (5)
11 Wise Men (4)
13 Mineral spring (3)

CROSSWORD
a Day!

ACROSS

1 Normal, typical (5)
3 Distinctive period (3)
6 Worthless dog (3)
7 Giver (5)
9 Rough flat boat (4)
11 Formal party (4)
13 Chipper (5)
14 Deep hole (3)
15 Peculiar (3)
16 Italian sauce (5)

DOWN

1 Stomach complaint (5)
4 Grumble (5)
5 Seabird (5)
8 Investment (5)
10 In front (5)
12 Game of chance (5)

DAY 329

CROSSWORD a Day!

ACROSS
1 Nightstick (9)
6 Openly shown (5)
7 Spirit (3)
8 Potter's material (4)
10 Remain (4)
13 Behave (3)
14 Style from a former era (5)
15 Play, A --- Named Desire (9)

DOWN
2 Challenger (5)
3 Metropolis (4)
4 Beatles' song, --- Days A Week (5)
5 Ronald Reagan's wife (5)
8 Set of students (5)
9 Make adjustments to (5)
11 Part of the heart (5)
12 Genuine (4)

DAY 330

CROSSWORD a Day!

ACROSS
1 Heroic poem (4)
3 Recedes (4)
6 Reek, stench (5)
7 Type of engine (3)
8 Crying (7)
13 Hospital section (1,1,1)
14 --- Picasso, artist (5)
15 *Van Helsing* actress, --- Beckinsale (4)
16 Television award (4)

DOWN
1 Compass direction (4)
2 Cuban dance (5)
4 Compact (house) (5)
5 Web page (4)
9 Explode (5)
10 Paint fragment (5)
11 Sample with the tongue (4)
12 Angular (body) (4)

DAY 331

CROSSWORD a Day!

ACROSS
1. Julius Caesar, eg (5)
4. Uppermost part (3)
5. Make incoherent (8)
7. Attract (4)
8. Notice (4)
11. Artistic (8)
13. Wiretap (3)
14. Actress, --- O'Neal (5)

DOWN
1. Teaser (6)
2. Scrooge (5)
3. Corner, recess (4)
4. Browned skin (3)
6. Waterway (6)
9. Decorate (walls) (5)
10. Would like (4)
12. Old piece of material (3)

CROSSWORD a Day!

ACROSS

1 Cut of meat (5)
4 Steal from (3)
6 Mesh bag (3)
8 Entice (5)
12 French cheese (4)
13 Chimney dust (4)
14 Entirety (5)
17 Stitched edge (3)
19 Procure (3)
20 Every 24 hours (5)

DOWN

1 Immoral act (3)
2 Newt (3)
3 Gear (3)
4 Caribbean spirit (3)
5 Nocturnal mammal (3)
7 Our planet (5)
9 Minimize (pain) (4)
10 Writing (5)
11 Healthy (4)
14 Toupee (3)
15 Not at home (3)
16 Tip (3)
17 Rabble, --- polloi (3)
18 Month (3)

DAY 333

CROSSWORD a Day!

ACROSS

1 Number of seasons (4)
3 Musical instrument (4)
7 Game (9)
8 Limb (3)
10 Route (3)
12 Animals who store nuts (9)
13 Regulation (4)
14 Brave person (4)

DOWN

2 Express views (5)
4 Dart (5)
5 Demanding (5)
6 North American waterfall (7)
8 No-hoper (5)
9 Oliver Twist's food (5)
11 Harmonica player, Larry --- (5)

CROSSWORD
a Day!

ACROSS
1 Serving board (4)
3 Lean (against) (4)
7 Set (8)
9 Female chicken (3)
10 Former (3)
14 Without moisture (3)
15 Give confidence (8)
16 Fortified wine (4)
17 Mischievous child (4)

DOWN
2 Vertical part of a stair (5)
4 Remove water from a boat (4)
5 Spinning tops, eg (4)
6 Unfocused (7)
8 Above, touching (2)
11 Brook (5)
12 Stumble (4)
13 Carnival (4)
14 Physician's title (2)

ACROSS
1 Ringing sound (5)
3 Snake (3)
6 Walk through water (4)
7 Very unattractive (4)
8 Sandwich filling with mustard (5,4)
13 Have committed to memory (4)
14 Guitarist, --- Hendrix (4)
15 Have a flutter (3)
16 Prominent person (5)

DOWN
1 Cringe (5)
2 Bollywood country (5)
4 Answer (a mystery) (5)
5 Unable to speak (4)
9 Small amount (5)
10 Planted (seeds) (4)
11 Improve the mind (5)
12 Put on (5)

LAGOON BOOKS

DAY 336

CROSSWORD
a Day!

Across
1 Chess player, --- Fischer (5)
5 Theatrical award (4)
8 Haphazard (6)
9 Outsized (clothing) (1,1)
11 I refuse (2)
12 Accident (6)
14 Hawaiian island (4)
15 Spaghetti, eg (5)

Down
2 Not written on (5)
3 Albanian king (3)
4 One-eyed monster (7)
6 Richard ---, entrepreneur (7)
7 Actress, --- Day (5)
10 Singer, --- Isaak (5)
13 Byron poem, --- *Walks In Beauty* (3)

SOLUTION FOR DAY 335
Across 1. Clink 3. Asp 6. Wade 7. Ugly 8. Roast beef 13. Know 14. Jimi 15. Bet 16. Doyen
Down 1. Cower 2. India 4. Solve 5. Dumb 9. Ounce 10. Sown 11. Edify 12. Feign

CROSSWORD a Day!

ACROSS

1 Belief in destiny (8)
6 Female heir (8)
8 Painful emotion (4)
9 Film, --- *High* (4)
12 Sudden (rise to success) (8)
14 Provide water to (8)

DOWN

2 Improve skills (5)
3 Danish toy bricks (4)
4 Take (an exam) (3)
5 Innovative, edgy (5)
7 Foam (5)
10 Great Wall country (5)
11 UN Secretary General, --- Annan (4)
13 Sailor (3)

CROSSWORD a Day!

ACROSS
- **1** Go backwards (in development) (7)
- **6** And others (2,2)
- **8** Lois ---, Clark Kent's colleague (4)
- **11** Refreshing beer (5)
- **12** Virginia ---, actress (4)
- **14** Mountain range (4)
- **15** (Within) view (7)

DOWN
- **2** Styling product (3)
- **3** Conger, eg (3)
- **4** Scent (7)
- **5** For the reason that (7)
- **7** Metal mixture (5)
- **9** Month (5)
- **10** Sense of self (3)
- **13** Keats poem, --- on Melancholy (3)
- **14** Grey dust (3)

DAY 339

CROSSWORD
a Day!

ACROSS
- 3 Benefit (4)
- 5 Sensual (6)
- 6 Amiss (4)
- 7 Loquacious (9)
- 10 Lower part of wall (4)
- 11 King of the fairies (6)
- 12 Consider (4)

DOWN
- 1 Raising agent (5)
- 2 Place to store goods (9)
- 3 Sprinkled (9)
- 4 Russian ballet company (5)
- 8 Stun (5)
- 9 African antelope (5)

SOLUTION FOR DAY 338

Across 1. Regress 6. Et al 8. Lane 11. Lager 12. Mayo 14. Alps 15. Eyeshot
Down 2. Gel 3. Eel 4. Perfume 5. Because 7. Alloy 9. April 10. Ego 13. *Ode* 14. Ash

DAY 340

CROSSWORD
a Day!

ACROSS
1 Firestarter? (5)
5 Request (4)
8 Landing strip (6)
9 Three-toed sloth (2)]
11 You (archaic) (2)
12 Ship's kitchen (6)
14 Source (4)
15 Cushion stuffing (5)

DOWN
2 Flimsy (metal) (5)
3 Yasser Arafat's
  party (1,1,1)
4 Icon, --- Monroe (7)
6 Addresses
  to God (7)
7 --- Michelle
  Gellar, actress (5)
10 Fall in prices (5)
13 Bend at the waist
  as a greeting (3)

SOLUTION FOR DAY 339

Across 3. Sake 5. Erotic 6. Awry 7. Talkative 10. Dado 11. Oberon 12. Deem
Down 1. Yeast 2. Stockroom 3. Scattered 4. Kirov 8. Amaze 9. Eland

CROSSWORD
a Day!

ACROSS

3 --- de Palma, film director (5)
6 Solitary person (5)
7 Billy ---, singer (5)
8 Hanging decoration (7)
12 *Aida*, eg (5)
14 Extra, back-up (5)
15 Dapper (5)

DOWN

1 Shanty town (4)
2 --- Previn, conductor (5)
3 Transmit (by radio wave) (9)
4 Frozen water (3)
5 Not any (4)
9 Wanderer (5)
10 Defeat (4)
11 Seven days (4)
13 Epoch (3)

CROSSWORD a Day!

ACROSS
1 Blaze (4)
3 Graceful bird (4)
7 Next (to) (8)
9 High mammal (3)
10 Immature frog (7)
13 Writing fluid (3)
14 Historical legwear (8)
15 Consumes (4)
16 Team (4)

DOWN
2 Improper (5)
4 Bike trick (7)
5 Memo (4)
6 Group including Frank Sinatra and Dean Martin (3,4)
8 *Mommie ---*, film (7)
11 Be subsequent (5)
12 Woodwind instrument (4)

CROSSWORD
a Day!

ACROSS
1 Farm animals (9)
6 Sandy shore (5)
7 Latest information (4)
9 Town ---, proclaimer (5)
10 Rob during a riot (4)
12 Soft, fluffy (5)
13 State of expectation! (9)

DOWN
2 Brainwave (4)
3 Accompany (6)
4 Different (5)
5 Booth, stall (5)
7 Space cloud (6)
8 Wheel lock (5)
9 Patch of trees (5)
11 Musician, --- Clapton (4)

CROSSWORD
a Day!

ACROSS
1. Frozen spike (6)
6. Piece of foliage (4)
7. Black Sea peninsula (6)
9. Lush, drunkard (9)
11. Planet (6)
12. Impoverished (4)
13. Hole for a shoelace (6)

DOWN
2. Equilateral ellipse (6)
3. External calm (9)
4. Complicated, detailed (9)
5. On holiday (3)
8. Body shape (6)
10. Select (3)

CROSSWORD
a Day!

ACROSS
3 Half note (5)
6 Jot (4)
7 Artificial hill (5)
8 Film approver (6)
10 French dance (6)
11 Pastoral (5)
12 Marshlands (4)
13 Cartoon character,
   --- Fudd (5)

DOWN
1 Dialogue (9)
2 Make amends (5)
4 Composer,
   --- Novello (4)
5 Art movement (9)
7 Conclusion of
   a fable (5)
9 Threaded nail (5)
10 Pudding (4)

CROSSWORD
a Day!

ACROSS

1 Hoax (4)
3 Egyptian goddess (4)
7 Convey (goods) (9)
8 Take from under someone's nose (3)
10 Stray (3)
12 Fruit bat (6,3)
13 Nickname for an American (4)
14 *Gorillas in the* ---, film (4)

DOWN

2 Approximately (5)
4 Make of pottery (5)
5 Greek wood god (5)
6 Sending out (7)
8 Adroit (5)
9 Musician, --- Ferry (5)
11 Chess castles (5)

CROSSWORD
a Day!

ACROSS
1 Mount ---, Ark's landing place (5)
5 Give way (to) (4)
6 Rather shocking (5)
8 Queen Victoria's husband (6)
10 Underlying (6)
12 Stupid person (5)
13 Buzz, rush (4)
14 Garment (5)

DOWN
1 Six-pointed shape (9)
2 Distinctive quality surrounding someone (4)
3 Mutineer (5)
4 Relevant (9)
7 Huge antelope (5)
9 Merchandise (5)
11 Ivory source (4)

CROSSWORD a Day!

ACROSS
3 Rodent (4)
5 Give pleasure to (6)
6 Mechanical memory (4)
7 Rule for solving mathematical problem (9)
10 Marco ---, explorer (4)
11 House's yard (6)
12 Extremely (4)

DOWN
1 --- Kahlo, painter (5)
2 Lives of the saints (9)
3 Wormlike (9)
4 Door catch (5)
8 Unpackaged (5)
9 A A ---, creator of Winnie-the-Pooh (5)

DAY 349

CROSSWORD a Day!

ACROSS

1 Forbidden (5)
3 Chop (3)
6 Lay level (4)
7 Units of current (4)
8 Pond plant (5,4)
13 Seaside jetty (4)
14 Dairy product (4)
15 Auction item (3)
16 Shy, nervous (5)

DOWN

1 Chuck (5)
2 *Carmen* composer (5)
4 Banish (5)
5 Yacht part (4)
9 Protein-making acid (5)
10 Irish republic (4)
11 Phrase (5)
12 Harnessed (oxen) (5)

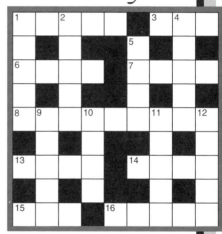

DAY 350

CROSSWORD a Day!

ACROSS
4 Win a Date with --- Hamilton, film (3)
6 Imply, --- to (6)
7 Witch (9)
10 Astronaut's outfit (9)
12 Diving duck (6)
13 Draw (out supplies) (3)

DOWN
1 Blackcurrant syrup (6)
2 Singer, --- Estefan (6)
3 Loyalty (9)
5 Helps (4)
8 Value of a house over its mortgage (6)
9 Planet (6)
11 Film, The --- Panther (4)

CROSSWORD
a Day!

ACROSS
1 & 4A Far Eastern financial capital (4,4)
4 See 1A
7 Unrealistic hope (4,5)
8 Docile (4)
10 Ali ---, legendary character (4)
12 Jockey's ride (9)
13 Deceased (4)
14 Mallard, eg (4)

DOWN
2 Board for communicating with spirits (5)
3 Ganders' mates (5)
5 Sung drama (5)
6 Greek letter (5)
8 Worn out (5)
9 Holy city (5)
10 Set of offspring (5)
11 Rudimentary (5)

SOLUTION FOR DAY 350

Across 4. *Tad* 6. Allude 7. Sorceress 10. Spacesuit 12. Scoter 13. Eke
Down 1. Cassis 2. Gloria 3. Adherence 5. Aida 8. Equity 9. Saturn 11. *Pink*

CROSSWORD
a Day!

ACROSS
1 Attendance (8)
5 Rage (3)
6 Cabaret show (5)
7 Schedule of duty (4)
9 Hand out (4)
13 Sweets (5)
14 Label (3)
15 Distance, put off (8)

DOWN
1 Previous (5)
2 Make an effort, --- oneself (5)
3 Deserve (4)
4 Praise worshipfully (5)
8 Japanese city (5)
10 Bit-part actor (5)
11 Two under par (5)
12 Wood pile for cremation (4)

CROSSWORD a Day!

ACROSS
1 Out of practice (5)
5 Part of an animal (4)
8 Allocate (6)
9 You and I (2)
11 Therefore (2)
12 Mohair (6)
14 Cut (a film) (4)
15 Summit of a wave (5)

DOWN
2 Fit (5)
3 Mandible (3)
4 Against the law (7)
6 Herb (7)
7 Actor's representative (5)
10 Compel (5)
13 Fasten (3)

CROSSWORD
a Day!

ACROSS
1 Actor, --- Torn (3)
3 Stylish (4)
5 Genetic copy (5)
6 Knight's title (3)
8 Harvest (4)
9 Bird (4)
11 *All About ---*, film (3)
13 Religion (5)
14 Stall, display (5)
15 Digit (3)

DOWN
1 Use again (7)
2 Upgrade (7)
3 Oscar-winning actress (4)
4 Animation technique in *Toy Story* (1,1,1)
6 Undermine (7)
7 Remnant (7)
10 Corrosive (4)
12 Check (3)

DAY 355

CROSSWORD a Day!

ACROSS

1 Horizontal mine entrance (4)
3 Broadcasting system (1,1,1,1)
7 Thin biscuit (5)
8 World Wide Web page address (1,1,1)
9 Lord of the Flies (9)
12 Diamonds (3)
13 Hangman's loop (5)
14 Items for unlocking doors (4)
15 Spoil, --- upon (4)

DOWN

2 Curtain (5)
4 Digit (5)
5 Biblical character (5)
6 *Raising* ---, film (7)
9 Flick eyelids shut (5)
10 *Behind --- Lines*, film (5)
11 Down (5)

LAGOON BOOKS

DAY 356

CROSSWORD
a Day!

ACROSS
1 Fortune, chance (4)
3 Church recess (4)
7 Tier (5)
8 Trim (3)
9 Europe's former currency (3)
10 Ironic (3)
11 Cellphone card (3)
13 Dance, --- de deux (3)
14 Possessor (5)
15 Smallest of a litter (4)
16 Move casually (4)

DOWN
1 Red ---, cheese (9)
2 Young stallion (4)
4 Unsullied (4)
5 Outing (9)
6 Street water pipe (7)
12 Low murmur of pain (4)
13 Ship's front (4)

DAY 357

CROSSWORD
a Day!

ACROSS
1 Express gratitude (5)
6 Remove, rub out (5)
7 Extinguish (5)
9 Aircraft's storage area (4)
10 Spring's shape (4)
14 Bait, goad (5)
15 Distress signal (5)
16 Rove in search of prey (5)

DOWN
2 Crested bird (6)
3 Bottom of a ship (4)
4 Cleaning cloth (3)
5 Original (3)
8 Children's puzzle (6)
11 Stage (4)
12 Many times (3)
13 Kiss of peace (3)

CROSSWORD
a Day!

ACROSS
1 Fruit (4)
5 Faddist (5)
7 Difficult, inconvenient (7)
8 Gusto (7)
11 Go forward (7)
13 --- O'Donnell, comic celebrity (5)
14 Actor, --- Baldwin (4)

DOWN
1 Irish fuel (4)
2 Bill Clinton's state (8)
3 Make a mistake (3)
4 Dance along (4)
5 Prisoner (7)
6 Attached (8)
9 Disease source? (4)
10 Steering apparatus (4)
12 Playing cube (3)

CROSSWORD a Day!

ACROSS

1 Light rain (7)
6 Toddler (3)
7 Eye make-up (7)
8 Camping shelter (4)
9 Urgently (1,1,1,1)
12 Great joy (7)
14 *For Me And My ---*, musical (3)
15 Imaginary ideal (7)

DOWN

1 Film, *The --- Busters* (3)
2 Writer of *Hedda Gabler* (5)
3 Enthusiasm (4)
4 Greek letter (3)
5 Terence ---, actor (5)
8 Trace (5)
10 Hindu god (5)
11 James ---, actor (4)
12 Imp (3)
13 Negative vote (3)

CROSSWORD a Day!

ACROSS

1 Two-way (radio) (1,1)
2 Clan (5)
7 Gird up your ---, prepare for energetic action (5)
8 *The Matrix* character (3)
9 Agreeable (4)
10 Strike of the whip (4)
12 Ram's mate (3)
13 Japanese poem (5)
14 Expensive (5)
15 Woman's title (2)

DOWN

1 Tube shape (8)
3 Lift up (4)
4 *Private* ---, film (8)
5 Trustworthy (8)
6 Riding breeches (8)
11 Loafer, eg (4)

DAY 361

CROSSWORD a Day!

ACROSS
2 Tungsten (7)
5 Deport (9)
7 Unpolished (5)
12 Element K (9)
14 Defensive mound (7)

DOWN
1 Consecrate (5)
2 H2O (5)
3 Fallow land (3)
4 Sculpture and music, eg (4)
6 Excavation (3)
8 Gametes (3)
9 Pole side of a flag (5)
10 Actor, --- Lee Jones (5)
11 Fizzy drink (4)
13 Ocean (3)

CROSSWORD a Day!

ACROSS
1 Sound of speech (5)
3 Request (3)
6 Bundle (3)
7 Unpaid servant (5)
9 Wound dressing (4)
11 Cat's lives! (4)
13 Stick (5)
14 Evergreen (3)
15 Mineral vein (3)
16 Southern US states (5)

DOWN
1 Type of letter (5)
4 Brad Pitt film (5)
5 Brief affair (5)
8 Long thin piece (5)
10 Read between the lines (5)
12 Mountain-top resort (5)

DAY 363

CROSSWORD a Day!

ACROSS
1 Welsh mountain range (9)
6 Dignified (5)
7 Organ scan (1,1,1)
8 Prison room (4)
10 Snake ---, double 1 on dice (4)
13 Musician, --- Stevens (3)
14 Plant part (5)
15 Consequential (9)

DOWN
2 Cheekiness (5)
3 ---, Where's My Car? film (4)
4 Leonard ---, actor (5)
5 Wrong (5)
8 Mexican plants? (5)
9 Respite (3-2)
11 Actress, --- Barkin (5)
12 Tart (4)

CROSSWORD
a Day!

ACROSS
1 Cover (4)
3 Heavy falling sound (4)
6 Answer (5)
7 Jug rim (3)
8 Facial feature (7)
13 Scent, --- de toilette (3)
14 Ghost (5)
15 Twilight (4)
16 Sunrise (4)

DOWN
1 Distort (4)
2 Legume (5)
4 Film, --- *Dolly!* (5)
5 Con (4)
9 Letter sign-off (5)
10 Fast (5)
11 Chief (4)
12 Body layer (4)

LAGOON BOOKS

DAY 365

CROSSWORD a Day!

ACROSS
1 Door part (5)
4 Success (3)
5 Large-eyed animal (8)
7 Melodic accent (4)
8 Nymph (4)
11 Absent-minded reverie (8)
13 Rent out (3)
14 --- Flynn, actor (5)

DOWN
1 Limp (6)
2 Of the nose (5)
3 Italian island (4)
4 Wheel part (3)
6 Ritualized (6)
9 Remove contents (5)
10 Inactive (4)
12 Worker or queen? (3)